The Greenwich Guides to Astronomy

The *Greenwich Guides* are a series of books on astronomy for the beginner. Each volume stands on its own but together they provide a complete introduction to the night sky, everything it contains, and how astronomers are discovering its secrets. Written by experts from the Old Royal Observatory at Greenwich, they are right up to date with the latest information from space exploration and research and are suitable for observers in both the northern and southern hemisphere.

Available now
The Greenwich Guide to Stargazing
The Greenwich Guide to The Planets

To be published
The Greenwich Guide to Stars, Galaxies and Nebulae
The Greenwich Guide to Astronomy in Action

The Old Royal Observatory, Greenwich, London is open daily to visitors. It is the home of Greenwich Mean Time and the Greenwich Meridian which divides East from West. It also houses the largest refracting telescope in Great Britain.

For more information write to: Marketing Department, National Maritime Museum, Greenwich, London SE10 9NF.

The Greenwich Guide to
Stargazing

Carole Stott

George Philip
 in association with
The National Maritime Museum, London

British Library Cataloguing in Publication Data

Stott, Carole
    The Greenwich Guide to Stargazing.
    1. Stars—Observers' manuals
    I. Title   II. Greenwich, Royal Observatory
    523.8   QB64
ISBN 0-540-01127-4

© The Trustees of the National Maritime Museum 1987
First published by George Philip,
27A Floral Street, London WC2E 9DP

Printed in Hong Kong

Acknowledgements

I am grateful to many people for their assistance in the preparation of this book. In particular I would like to thank Marilla Fletcher, Stuart Malin and other colleagues at the Old Royal Observatory, Greenwich, David Hughes of Sheffield University and Lydia Greeves of George Philip.

I am also grateful to the following for permission to reproduce their illustrations: Bodleian Library, Oxford, MS Marsh 144 p. 19; Anthony Drennan pp. 20, 21 (top left and bottom); European Southern Observatory p. 45; Federation of Astronomical Societies, p. 12 (Robin Scagell), pp. 13, 87 (Geoff Pearce), p. 38 (bottom) (Bill O'Shaugnessy), p. 39 (Ruth Bradford-Harris), pp. 42, 50, 53 (Raymond Livori), pp. 48, 93 (David Early), p. 51 (Ron Arbour), p. 62 (John Laidlaw), p. 92 (Anthony Thomas); Harry Ford p. 86; Robert McNaught pp. 2, 47; NASA p. 85; The Trustees, The National Gallery, London p. 46; The Trustees, The National Maritime Museum, London pp. 8, 18, 21, pp. 9, 29, 88, 90 (Jim Stevenson); Martin Ratcliffe pp. 34, 84; Royal Greenwich Observatory, Herstmonceux p. 27 (David Calvert); all the star maps except those on pp. 10 and 11 were drawn by Wil Tirion.

Jacket illustrations: Federation of Astronomical Societies, Ron Arbour (front); Old Royal Observatory, Jim Stevenson (back).

TITLE-PAGE ILLUSTRATION *The star-studded sky of the southern hemisphere.*

Contents

Introduction

At first glance the night sky seems to be a confusing mass of stars. The pin-points of light all look very much the same and seem to be scattered at random across the sky. But in fact with very little effort anyone can begin to recognize the star patterns that have been known since ancient times. This book is aimed at the novice stargazer who wants to recognize these constellations and the fascinating objects they contain. It provides basic, practical hints as well as maps which will help you find your way about the sky, wherever you are and whatever the season. There are chapters on double and variable stars, on the deep sky objects—galaxies, star clusters and nebulae—and on our local star, the Sun. This book shows you that you do not need expensive equipment to be a stargazer. Your eyes, this book and some patience is all its takes. It's the best show around and it's just waiting for you to start watching.

1 · Finding your Way amongst the Stars

Stargazing can be as simple or as difficult as you want to make it. Weather permitting, the stars are available for everyone to see and enjoy. You may just want to 'sightsee'—simply basking in the romance and splendour of the star-studded heavens—or to follow the changing spectacle of the night sky more closely, at different times and from various locations. This book is intended to act as a guide for the sightseer, pointing out the highlights of the stargazer's tour as time and location change. Starting with the simple star patterns in the sky, it moves on to the details of individual stars, and then to star clusters and whole galaxies. Using this book you can discover these for yourself. The basic outline of the natural history of stars is also covered, although the full details can be found in a separate volume of this series of four books.

We have been looking up at the sky ever since the birth of man, watching the stars with interest and admiration. The knowledge that ancient man acquired about the heavens is easily attained by anyone today. No sophisticated or expensive instruments are necessary. A trained naked eye will find its way amongst the stars using recognized signposts to move from star to star, or group to group, just as man has always done. Most people have the impression that there are millions of stars in the sky and that the job of recognizing constellations is very difficult. It's not. People who live in large cities, with pollution and street lighting, will only see about 300 stars above the horizon at any one time on a clear moonless night. It's immediately obvious that these have a range of brightness and that the

bright stars seem to be grouped, making up a series of rather odd, different, sparkling patterns.

The very first stargazers divided the sky into regions to help them find their way about the starry sphere. Each region contained five to ten bright stars. Figures or creatures whose shapes were suggested by these groups of stars were used to help recall a sky region. These constellation figures have been passed on to us and, with some modifications and additions, they are what we use today to find our way about the sky. Some of these constellations do resemble their names. It is easy enough to draw a crouching lion around the stars in Leo, and a bull's head around those in Taurus, but it needs good imagination to picture the stars of Cassiopeia as the Queen of Ethiopia sitting in a chair. You might find it easier to recognize certain groups of stars by creating your own pictures although you will still need to be aware of the internationally recognized constellations and their names. There are eighty-eight of these covering the complete sky. A selection of them are described in Chapter 7. They have been chosen for their distribution about the sky and because they contain interesting objects, as well as because they are easy to find.

As the Earth spins it reveals an ever-changing view of the heavens. This means that we see our local star, the Sun, crossing our sky during the day. Its regular apparent movement is familiar to us. Less familiar is the apparent movement of the stars. As the Earth continues on its daily spin, the light and warmth of the Sun fade and are replaced by a colder, darker, star-studded sky. Regular sky watchers will see that the stars

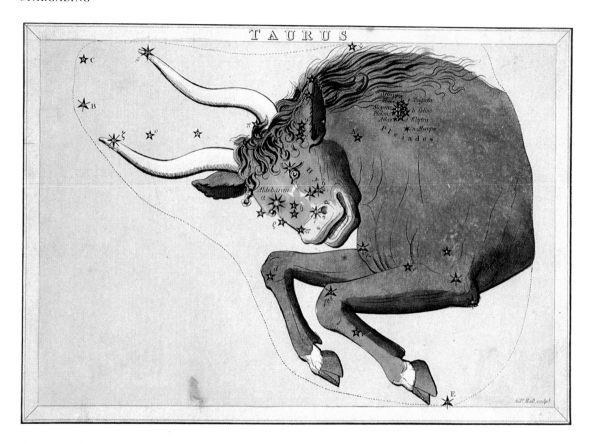

The stars in the constellation of Taurus form a dominant 'V' shape which marks the bull's face. The bull's horns stretch out to two single bright stars. It is easy enough to imagine the outline of the bull around these stars in the sky, and to use it as a means of identifying the stars, but there are many groupings which are more difficult to reconcile with their name.

Chapter 7 has star maps for different locations throughout the year, but these are static pictures.

Should you want to see how your view of the sky changes, or to look at a sky map for another time or date or location than those shown here, then buy a planisphere. These are inexpensive and durable sky maps showing all the stars

appear to move across the night sky at about the same speed as the Sun did across the daytime sky. The path the stars follow is, however, different and depends on where you are observing from on Earth. The actual stars you see also differ according to the time of year and where you are.

RIGHT *The planisphere is a very useful tool for all astronomers. It is a star map which can be set to show the stars visible at a particular time and date. Planispheres are available for different locations throughout the world. It is only necessary to make sure you have the appropriate one for your latitude.*

visible from particular latitudes. A movable window over the star background shows the stars visible at any particular date and time. Both experienced and novice astronomers use planispheres. They are easy and quick to consult and can be easily placed in a suitcase when going on holiday. Taking one with you wherever you go is a good habit to develop. Holiday locations are usually away from busy cities and so offer skies free from light pollution. Do remember to take the planisphere which is relevant to the latitude of the place where you're going on holiday. Although there is no need to spend any money to be a stargazer, a planisphere is one of the best things you can buy; so put it high on your shopping list.

You may even be keen to buy a telescope, as many people believe that astronomers and telescopes are inseparable. But neither a telescope nor binoculars (which can be a better alternative) are essential. Become a competent naked-eye observer first and once you know the type of astronomy you are interested in you can then decide if you need an instrument, and what type you should get. First you need to find your way around the sky. Until you know what you are looking at there is little point in trying to get a better view of it.

The trickiest part of becoming a stargazer is to find your first signpost in the sky. Once you have identified a constellation on your own you have taken that first step. Choose one of the easily recognizable constellations to start off with and then move from this to other easy ones. Then progress from these to their neighbours, slowly moving away from your original base. Before you know it you'll have moved across the sky, hopping from constellation to constellation, or from bright star to bright star. You may like to follow an obvious or standard route or to develop your own. When we travel around on Earth there are standard routes to follow. If you were going from London to Bristol in England you would probably start and finish the journey on a motorway; a direct route which does not go through another town or city. An alternative would be to follow signposts from London to Reading, then directions from Reading to Bath, and finally a route from Bath to Bristol. You still finish in Bristol but the route you have followed will be different; one that you may or may not prefer.

Here are three routes, or star-hopping procedures that you can follow depending on whether you are observing from northern, equatorial or southern latitudes on Earth. As when planning any journey, study them first before trying them out. With any map, until you have tried the route once you don't know quite what to expect. The difficult part is comparing a map to reality. The distances between the stars in the sky are usually greater than most people expect from just looking at a map. The route will, however, get easier and more familiar each time you follow it.

The northern sky

There are five major constellations which are always visible in the northern sky. Whatever time of year it is you can use these five as your starting points. They are: Ursa Major (the Great

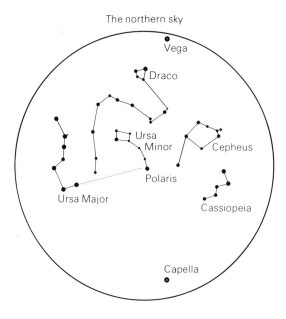

ABOVE *The northern sky. These constellation patterns and bright stars are always above the horizon, and so are visible throughout the year to observers in northern latitudes. They can be used as a starting point for a more extensive study of the northern hemisphere sky.*

Bear), Ursa Minor (the Lesser Bear), Cassiopeia, Cepheus and Draco (the Dragon). Many people who would not claim to be stargazers know Ursa Major. Or, more correctly, they know a part of Ursa Major, the seven bright stars called the Plough, or Big Dipper, which you may find easier to think of as a saucepan. The two stars on the side of the pan away from the handle point directly to Polaris. This star is known as the Pole Star because it is so close to the north celestial pole. It is the brightest star in Ursa Minor, a smaller and less obvious constellation but otherwise of similar shape to the Plough. Snaking between these two constellations is Draco, its tail closest to the two pointers in the Plough. At an equal distance from Polaris and almost opposite Ursa Major is Cassiopeia, the Queen of Ethiopia. Between her and Draco is Cepheus, her king.

These and all the other northern constellations appear to move around Polaris, the Pole Star, so be prepared to look for Cassiopeia as either an 'M' above the Pole or a 'W' underneath it, depending on the time of night. Look at the maps in Chapter 7 to see exactly how things will look at the time you want to observe. You can move further away from Polaris by picking up the bright star Vega in Lyra; and in a position almost equal in distance from Polaris, and diagonally opposite Vega, is Capella in the constellation Auriga.

The southern sky

As in the case of the northern sky, the southern stars also appear to rotate about a point and it is useful to use the stars around this point as stepping-stones to other constellations. Unfortunately there is no star that conveniently marks the southern celestial pole in the way that Polaris marks the northern. There is, however, a dominant constellation nearby—Crux, the

LEFT *The stars of the Plough as depicted by Van Gogh. This is arguably the most easily recognized and the best known of all star patterns.*

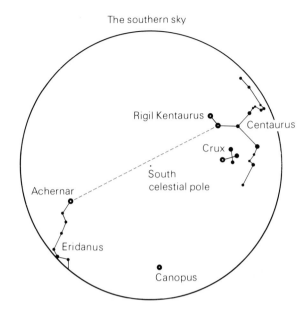

The southern sky

Rigil Kentaurus ● Centaurus

Crux

South celestial pole

Achernar

Eridanus

Canopus

ABOVE *The southern sky. Just as the stars centred on the north celestial pole are only visible to northern hemisphere observers, these southern stars are only visible to southern hemisphere observers. Crux is the dominant constellation and can be used as a stepping-stone to other stars.*

Southern Cross, known as well in the southern hemisphere as the Plough is in the northern. Near Crux is the third brightest star in the sky, Rigil Kentaurus of the constellation Centaurus, the Centaur. On the opposite side of the southern celestial pole is the bright star Achernar in the constellation of Eridanus. A third bright star to find is Canopus in Carina, the Keel, which is the second brightest star in the whole sky.

The equatorial sky

Constellations within this region of the sky can be seen not only by those living at equatorial latitudes, but also by northern and southern observers at certain times of the year. You can find out when they will be visible by looking at the seasonal maps in Chapter 7. Key constellations to look out for are Taurus (the Bull), Orion (the Hunter), Canis Major (the Greater Dog), Canis Minor (the Lesser Dog) and Gemini

BELOW *The equatorial sky. These constellations and bright stars are some of the easiest to identify. They can be seen by observers at northern, southern and equatorial latitudes, but not all at one time. Chapter 7 supplies the details.*

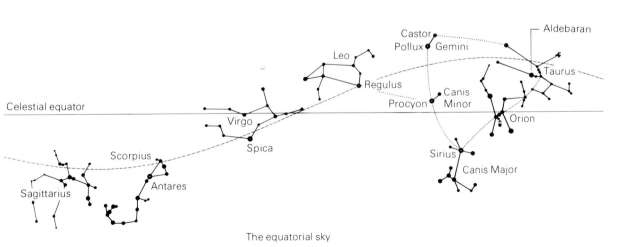

Castor
Pollux ● Gemini
Leo
Aldebaran
Regulus
Taurus
Celestial equator
Canis Minor
Procyon
Orion
Virgo
Spica
Scorpius
Sirius
Antares
Canis Major
Sagittarius

The equatorial sky

The constellation of Orion has a very distinctive shape. Here it is in the western sky, at springtime, in a view from southern England.

(the Twins) in one group, leading to Leo (the Lion), Virgo (the Virgin), Scorpius (the Scorpion) and Sagittarius (the Archer) stretching across the sky in a second grouping. All these constellations have distinctive star patterns or very prominent single stars which can act as stepping-stones over the heavens. The three stars that form the central belt in the distinctive shape of Orion point in one direction to Sirius in Canis Major, the brightest star in the sky, and in the opposite direction to the 'V' shape of stars that make up the bull's head in Taurus. The two stars that suggest the horns of the bull point to the two bright stars known as the Twins, Castor and Pollux. Lying almost equidistant between Pollux and Sirius is another bright star, Procyon of Canis Minor.

In the second elongated grouping three equally spaced bright stars, Regulus, Spica and Antares, lead us through their respective parent constellations of Leo, Virgo and Scorpius and on to the constellation of Sagittarius. Depending on when you are observing and where you are observing from it may not be possible to complete either of these tours through the sky. Each of the stars or constellations mentioned can be used as a starting or finishing point for your observing. These stepping-stones can also be linked with those in the northern and southern sky tours.

If you are ready to go outside and you are keen to start your stargazing journey before learning more, go straight to Chapter 9 for some practical advice on observing.

The constellation of Scorpius seen in the dark skies over Kenya in February. Antares is the bright red star towards the top and centre of the picture. The curve of the stars towards the bottom and centre form the scorpion's tail.

2 · The Story of the Constellations

Astronomy is the oldest of all the sciences. Even prehistoric man knew that the motions of the Sun and Moon affect the course of human life. Today we know and understand the laws behind the regular cycles of these bodies, but in earlier times people struggled to make sense of them. To help their calculations they mapped the principal star groups to act as a background to the Sun and Moon and planets. A system of constellations along the Sun's path, for example, made it easy to keep track of the Sun and could be used for agricultural and religious purposes, and for charting the progress of the year. The Sun's path against the background of stars is called the ecliptic. One circuit of this path is completed by the Sun each year. The band of sky centred on the ecliptic is the zodiac. The planets and the Moon as well as the Sun all move within the zodiac and so its constellations were amongst the first to be defined. They are Aries, Taurus, Gemini, Cancer, Leo, Virgo, Libra, Scorpius, Sagittarius, Capricornus, Aquarius and Pisces. The term zodiac derives from the Greek for animal, and this is still a circle of creatures. The one exception is Libra (the Scales), which was introduced long after the others. Other constellations off the ecliptic were used in navigation. This frame of reference across the heavens was essential for early astronomy and for land and sea navigation.

Breaking the star background up into areas and drawing familiar figures and animals in those areas is the best way to get to know the heavens. One way of doing this is to take a familiar figure and superimpose it on the sky and then use your imagination to make the stars fit the picture. Alternatively you can draw lines between the stars and create your own picture by 'joining the dots'. This second method may produce some weird and wonderful pictures, but how memorable would they be; could you recreate them time and time again? The first approach which uses familiar pictures is not only easier but has the advantage that your method and pictures can be used by others. Everyone can imagine a bear, a crab, a dog, or a fish and learn the star positions by tracing them out in the sky.

The zodiacal constellations form the backdrop for the movement of the Sun, Moon and planets as viewed from Earth.

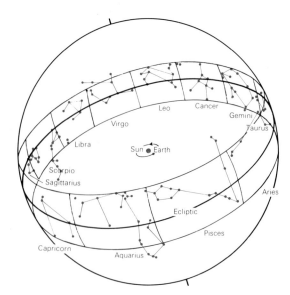

A system of charting all the sky in this way developed over the years and in 1930 the International Astronomical Union agreed on standard divisions. The table below lists the eighty-eight accepted constellations, with their Latin and common English names, the genitive form (used to denote 'belonging to') and its abbreviation. In general, individual stars are identified within a constellation by a letter of the Greek alphabet (see p. 96) followed by the genitive form of the constellation. For example α Andromedae identifies the star designated α (alpha = a in the Greek alphabet) belonging to the constellation of Andromeda.

Table of constellations

Name	Genitive	Abbreviation	Common name
Andromeda	Andromedae	And	Andromeda
Antlia	Antliae	Ant	The Air Pump
Apus	Apodis	Aps	The Bird of Paradise
Aquarius	Aquarii	Aqr	The Water Carrier
Aquila	Aquilae	Aql	The Eagle
Ara	Arae	Ara	The Altar
Aries	Arietis	Ari	The Ram
Auriga	Aurigae	Aur	The Charioteer
Boötes	Boötis	Boo	The Herdsman
Caelum	Caeli	Cae	The Engraving Tool
Camelopardalis	Camelopardalis	Cam	The Giraffe
Cancer	Cancri	Cnc	The Crab
Canes Venatici	Canum Venaticorum	CVn	The Hunting Dogs
Canis Major	Canis Majoris	CMa	The Greater Dog
Canis Minor	Canis Minoris	CMi	The Lesser Dog
Capricornus	Capricorni	Cap	The Sea Goat
Carina	Carinae	Car	The Keel
Cassiopeia	Cassiopeiae	Cas	Cassiopeia
Centaurus	Centauri	Cen	The Centaur
Cepheus	Cephei	Cep	Cepheus
Cetus	Ceti	Cet	The Whale
Chamaeleon	Chamaeleonis	Cha	The Chameleon
Circinus	Circini	Cir	The Pair of Compasses
Columba	Columbae	Col	The Dove
Coma Berenices	Coma Berenicis	Com	Berenice's Hair
Corona Australis	Coronae Australis	CrA	The Southern Crown
Corona Borealis	Coronae Borealis	CrB	The Northern Crown
Corvus	Corvi	Crv	The Crow
Crater	Crateris	Crt	The Cup

15

Name	Genitive	Abbreviation	Common name
Crux	Crucis	Cru	The Southern Cross
Cygnus	Cygni	Cyg	The Swan
Delphinus	Delphini	Del	The Dolphin
Dorado	Doradus	Dor	The Goldfish
Draco	Draconis	Dra	The Dragon
Equuleus	Equulei	Equ	The Little Horse
Eridanus	Eridani	Eri	The River Eridanus
Fornax	Fornacis	For	The Furnace
Gemini	Geminorum	Gem	The Twins
Grus	Gruis	Gru	The Crane
Hercules	Herculis	Her	Hercules
Horologium	Horologii	Hor	The Pendulum Clock
Hydra	Hydrae	Hya	The Water Snake
Hydrus	Hydri	Hyi	The Lesser Water Snake
Indus	Indi	Ind	The Indian
Lacerta	Lacertae	Lac	The Lizard
Leo	Leonis	Leo	The Lion
Leo Minor	Leonis Minoris	LMi	The Lesser Lion
Lepus	Leporis	Lep	The Hare
Libra	Librae	Lib	The Scales
Lupus	Lupi	Lup	The Wolf
Lynx	Lyncis	Lyn	The Lynx
Lyra	Lyrae	Lyr	The Lyre
Mensa	Mensae	Men	Table Mountain
Microscopium	Microscopii	Mic	The Microscope
Monoceros	Monocerotis	Mon	The Unicorn
Musca	Muscae	Mus	The Fly
Norma	Normae	Nor	The Level
Octans	Octantis	Oct	The Octant
Ophiuchus	Ophiuchi	Oph	The Serpent Holder
Orion	Orionis	Ori	Orion, the Hunter
Pavo	Pavonis	Pav	The Peacock
Pegasus	Pegasi	Peg	Pegasus
Perseus	Persei	Per	Perseus
Phoenix	Phoenicis	Phe	The Phoenix
Pictor	Pictoris	Pic	The Painter's Easel

Name	Genitive	Abbreviation	Common name
Pisces	Piscium	Psc	The Fishes
Piscis Austrinus	Piscis Austrini	PsA	The Southern Fish
Puppis	Puppis	Pup	The Stern
Pyxis	Pyxidis	Pyx	The Mariner's Compass
Reticulum	Reticuli	Ret	The Net
Sagitta	Sagittae	Sge	The Arrow
Sagittarius	Sagittarii	Sgr	The Archer
Scorpius	Scorpii	Sco	The Scorpion
Sculptor	Sculptoris	Scl	The Sculptor
Scutum	Scuti	Sct	The Shield
Serpens	Serpentis	Ser	The Serpent
Sextans	Sextantis	Sex	The Sextant
Taurus	Tauri	Tau	The Bull
Telescopium	Telescopii	Tel	The Telescope
Triangulum	Trianguli	Tri	The Triangle
Triangulum Australe	Trianguli Australis	TrA	The Southern Triangle
Tucana	Tucanae	Tuc	The Toucan
Ursa Major	Ursae Majoris	UMa	The Great Bear
Ursa Minor	Ursae Minoris	UMi	The Lesser Bear
Vela	Velorum	Vel	The Sail
Virgo	Virginis	Vir	The Virgin
Volans	Volantis	Vol	The Flying Fish
Vulpecula	Vulpeculae	Vul	The Fox

Some of these constellations, particularly those in the southern skies, were invented in modern times, so we know exactly how they arose, but others have much earlier beginnings.

Many constellation names and pictures, such as Andromeda or Orion, are not immediately familiar to someone of the twentieth century, but they would have been to people long ago. The names and images used in some of the constellations are a good indication of when they were first drawn. Figures like Orion, the Hunter, featured in Greek mythology. He threatened to exterminate all creatures on Earth and so the scorpion (Scorpius) was brought against him and stung him. A troop of divine maidens fled from Orion and were turned into the seven bright stars of the Pleiades. Others are based on tools of the arts and sciences. The astronomer Johannes Hevelius was the first to introduce a constellation of this type in the mid seventeenth century, basing Sextans on his own large sextant. Others were introduced by Lacaille in the mid eighteenth century, including Pictor (a painter's easel), Horologium (a pendulum clock), Caelum (an engraver's tool), Antlia (an air pump) and Fornax (a chemical furnace).

Other constellations were established much earlier and their origins are much more difficult to trace. A basic framework for dividing up the heavens had been firmly established by the time

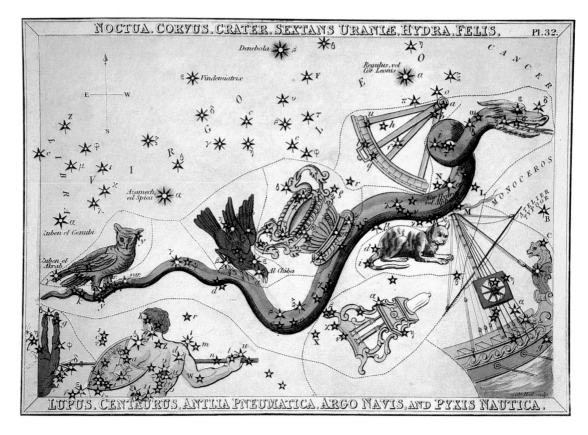

NOCTUA, CORVUS, CRATER, SEXTANS URANIÆ, HYDRA, FELIS. Pl. 32.

LUPUS, CENTAURUS, ANTLIA PNEUMATICA, ARGO NAVIS, AND PYXIS NAUTICA.

Some of the constellations introduced since the seventeenth century but now no longer in use are shown in this star chart of the 1830s.

of Ptolemy. He produced the *Almagest*, a handbook of mathematical astronomy, in *c.*AD 150. This contained a star catalogue which listed 1028 stars (1025 plus 3 duplicates). All the stars were visible from the Mediterranean and bright enough to be distinguished by the naked eye. They were grouped into forty-eight constellations: twelve along the ecliptic, twenty-one to the north and fifteen to the south. Ptolemy named a few individual stars, including Arcturus, Capella, Antares, Procyon and Canopus,

but generally identified a star within its constellation grouping, for example, 'the bright star in the tail' of the swan (α Cygni).

Ptolemy had been following ancient tradition and his work was partially based on earlier catalogues, in particular that of the astronomer Hipparchus in the second century BC. Although the earlier catalogues have been lost, we can trace the story of the original constellations back further than the time of Hipparchus. The earliest known description of our present constellation patterns was in the work of Eudoxus, who wrote in *c.*400 BC. This work, now lost, was used as the basis of a long astronomical poem written by Aratus around 250 BC. He described forty-three constellations and named five individual stars. Recent study has shown that the stellar descriptions in Aratus's poem are even older than was first thought and that they relate to an epoch of 2000 years BC plus or minus 200 years, and were observed from a latitude of 36°N plus or minus $1\frac{1}{2}°$.

We also know that the Babylonians had constellations resembling our own as far back as 2500 BC, and that by the same date the Minoans had a system of constellations by which they could navigate. The ancient Egyptians, too, had a framework of constellations—thirty-six circled the sky to the south of the ecliptic, and about twenty-five others covered the sky to north and south. Several royal Egyptian tombs of the second millennium BC include paintings of constellation figures. The unfinished tomb of the Egyptian nobleman Senmut (about 1473 BC) shows sky figures of a hippopotamus, a man, a lion and a crocodile. Yet only three ancient Egyptian configurations can be identified with any certainty: the Plough, which they showed as the foreleg of a bull and named Meskhetiu; Orion, represented as the god Osiris and the star Sirius, represented as the goddess Isis.

The Chinese and Indians developed independent systems. They divided the sky into twenty-eight parts, or lunar mansions, called *hsiu* in China and *nakshatra* in India. The Chinese first divided the sky into quarters as long ago as the fourteenth century BC and twenty-three *hsiu* are thought to go as far back as 850 BC. It is known that the Indian system was formed before 800 BC.

Ptolemy's star catalogue became the standard list of constellations for more than 1400 years. Both European and Islamic astronomers limited their observations to the stars in Ptolemy's list and all the new catalogues produced during this period were revisions of Ptolemy's. The notable catalogues were Al Sufi's in the tenth century, the Alphonsine Tables of the thirteenth century and those of Ulugh Beg and Copernicus in the

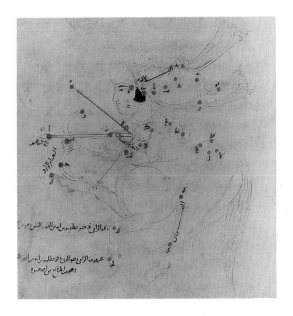

Sagittarius, the Archer, as depicted by Al Sufi in the tenth century. The constellation has been drawn as a mirror image of how it appears in the sky. As we look at Sagittarius from Earth he is shooting his arrow at the scorpion (Scorpius) to his right. Here the constellation is viewed from outside the celestial sphere and so the whole picture is reversed. This is how constellations are represented on celestial globes which means that although they are beautiful to look at they can confuse the stargazer.

fifteenth and sixteenth centuries respectively. It was not until the late sixteenth century and the work of the Landgrave William of Hesse and Tycho Brahe that the Ptolemaic stars were plotted with increased accuracy and non-Ptolemaic stars were systematically charted.

Tycho Brahe expanded the catalogue of northern stars. The southern stars were compiled by the Dutch navigators Pietr Dirksz Keyser and Frederick de Houtman, who were the first Europeans to chart the stars around the Antarctic pole. This work was refined and expanded when astronomers like Riccioli, Anselme and Hevelius used the ever-improving instruments on the northern stars and Edmond Halley worked on the southern stars. In the eighteenth century the stars of the northern hemisphere were recharted by John Flamsteed (from Greenwich) and Lalande, and those of the southern hemisphere by Lacaille.

Most of the stars in Ptolemy's catalogue fitted within his forty-eight constellation figures. The remaining stars were known as 'unformed' stars of a nearby constellation. Through extensive observations, voyages to the southern hemisphere and the revelations of the newly-invented telescope many more stars were discovered than those in Ptolemy's original list. Astronomers quickly formed these into constellations.

A number of new animal constellations were created. Some of those devised by Keyser and de Houtman were based on creatures recently discovered in the New World, and included Apus (a tropical bird), Chamaeleon, Dorado (a gold fish), Grus (a crane), Hydrus (a water snake), Musca (a fly), Pavo (a peacock), Tucana (a toucan) and Volans (a flying fish), as well as Indus (an American Indian) and Triangulum. We have Hevelius to thank for Canes Venatici (the hunting dogs), Lacerta (a lizard), Leo Minor (a small lion), Lynx and Vulpecula cum Ansere (a fox with a goose, although the goose has now flown). As the list on pp. 15–17 shows, all of these are still in use. Others proved less durable, among them Lalande's cat, Felis, and Le Monnier's Renne (a reindeer). These and thirteen small animal constellations devised by the Englishman John Hill were all short-lived.

Anybody could devise a new constellation, or redesign or remove an existing one, but a new one would only endure if it became popular with other astronomers and was copied by the mapmakers. It could achieve a permanent status only through common consent, as Hill discovered. He published his only astronomical book in 1754, in which he introduced his thirteen newly-invented constellations. These included Testudo (the tortoise) near Pisces, Lumbricus (the common earthworm), crawling from Canis Minor to Gemini, and Aranea (a long-legged spider), marching between the constellations of Virgo and Hydra, but none are used today.

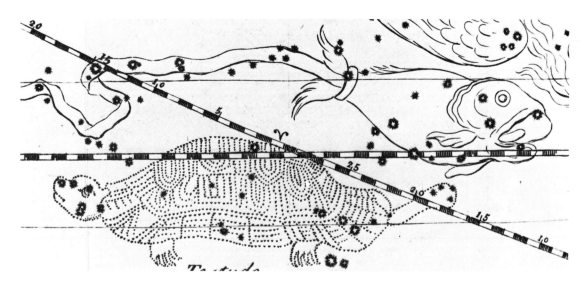

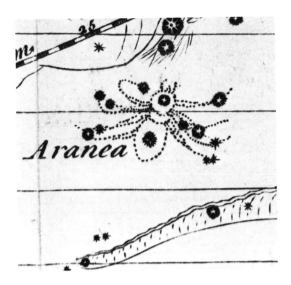

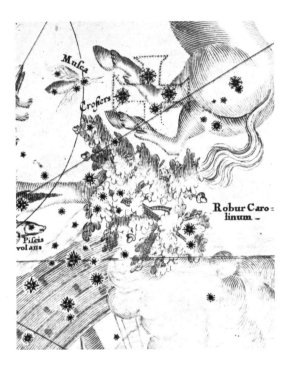

ABOVE, BELOW AND LEFT *A tortoise, an earthworm and a spider, three constellations which the Englishman John Hill attempted to introduce in the late eighteenth century.*

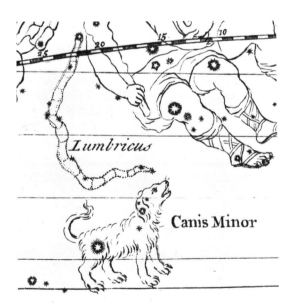

ABOVE *Robur Carolinum (Charles' oak), the short-lived constellation which Edmond Halley created and dedicated to King Charles II.*

Other new constellations were equally short-lived. With the religious wars of the Reformation and Counter-Reformation astronomers attempted to de-paganize the heavens. Crux (the Southern Cross) and Columba (Noah's dove) were created. Julius Schiller transformed the northern constellations into figures from the New Testament, the southern into notables from the Old Testament, and the zodiac signs into the twelve apostles. Some astronomers preferred to choose political subjects. Edmond Halley observed and named the constellation Robur Carolinum (Charles' oak), which represented the tree where Charles II hid from republican soldiers. Within a month of naming this constellation and presenting his southern sky map to the King,

21

Halley, who was later to go to Greenwich as second Astronomer Royal, was awarded an Oxford University degree by order of the King! Other politically derived constellations have included the crossed swords of the Electors of Saxony, the orb of the Emperor of Germany, the sceptre of Brandenburg, the shield of the King of Poland and the harp of the British King George III.

Star identification

As we saw on p. 15, the internationally recognized system of bright star identification is to use a letter from the Greek alphabet. The brightest star in the constellation is usually termed α (alpha), the second brightest β (beta) and so on. This system was introduced by the German astronomer Johann Bayer at the beginning of the seventeenth century and we now know that some stars should have been arranged in a slightly different order of brightness and that not all the stars in each constellation are included. For example, the brightest stars in Sagittarius, Orion and Gemini have been designated β. Under this system the letter of a star is written first and the genitive form of the constellation name follows it. For example, the brightest star in the constellation Leo is α Leonis, the second brightest β Leo and so on. The second star has been written here using the abbreviated form of the constellation name. Refer back to pp. 15–17 for the full list. The Greek alphabet is on p. 96.

One constellation that doesn't follow this rule is Lynx. The brightest star is referred to as α Lyncis but the rest of the stars have what are known as Flamsteed numbers, so called after England's first Astronomer Royal, John Flam-steed. Based at the Royal Observatory, Green-wich, he observed and then recorded the co-ordinates of 2935 stars in his catalogue *Historia Coelestis Britannica*, published in 1725. They were later depicted in his *Atlas Coelestis*, published in 1729. He identified his stars according to right ascension, the celestial equivalent of longitude on Earth (see p. 28). In Lynx you will find that the stars are denoted as 5 Lyn, 12 Lyn, 15 Lyn and so on. The numbers given to each star were added later by other astronomers. This system depends on the value of right ascension (RA); the greater the RA the greater the number. This method is also customarily used for faint stars which can be seen with the naked eye in all constellations.

Flamsteed's maps were amongst the first to make use of symbols and co-ordinates (celestial latitude and longitude) rather than the pictorial approach to the constellations, although the scientific renaissance had begun much earlier, at the same time as the development of printing and the widespread publication of maps, globes and books. The first important printed star maps were Albrecht Dürer's two planispheres of 1515, depicting the classical constellation figures. Alessandro Piccolomini's *De Le Stelle Fisse Libro Uno* of 1540 was the first to depict stars as distinct from pictures of constellations, while Giovanni Paolo Gallucci's star atlas of 1588 was the first to include co-ordinates. Other notable atlases were those of Johann Bayer (*Uranometria*, 1603), Johannes Hevelius (*Uranographia*, 1687), and Johann Elert Bode (*Uranographia*, 1801).

In addition to individual stars, constellations can contain star clusters, nebulous gas clouds and galaxies made up of vast numbers of stars (see Chapter 6). There is an easy system for identifying these objects too, but it does not refer to the parent constellation. Each star cluster or gas cloud etc. will have an 'M' number, an 'NGC' number, or both. The 'M' numbers were given to clusters and nebulae by the French astronomer Charles Messier in the late eighteenth century. He catalogued just over a hundred objects, all of which he believed were either star clusters or nebulae. His main reason for doing this was so that they would not be mistaken for comets. Astronomers since Messier have shown that his understanding of the term 'nebula' needed to be revised. His 'M' numbers refer to objects other than just star clusters and true nebulae, and in fact the list includes supernova remnants and galaxies. Almost all the objects in Messier's list also have 'NGC' numbers, relating to a more comprehensive list of thousands of objects known as the New General Catalogue. It was first published in 1888 and is still used by professional astronomers today, although the hundred or so Messier objects are usually referred to primarily by their 'M' numbers. For example, M42, also known as NGC 1976, is a gigantic nebula in the constellation Orion, often simply referred to as the Orion Nebula, while the Pleiades star cluster in Taurus is less well known as M45.

More recently published catalogues include many fainter stars that could not be detected with early instruments. They may easily contain around 300,000 stars. There are, however, many more modest catalogues and maps which are more suitable for the dedicated amateur than the long and detailed listings aimed at the professional should you want to pursue a greater range of stars than have been included in this book. They may not have the charm and beauty of the older atlases, but they'll certainly be more helpful when stargazing.

Many bright stars are more readily known by their individual names than they are by their Greek letter and parent constellation. For example, Polaris is less well known as α Ursae Minoris, or Castor and Pollux as α and β Geminorum respectively. As with the constellations the identification of individual stars can be traced back to the very earliest days of astronomy. As we have seen, Ptolemy is responsible for passing on some of the present names to us. Sirius (α Canis Majoris) and Arcturus (α Boötis), both of Greek origin, were used by him. He would, however, more usually identify a particular star by describing its position within a constellation. The star we now refer to as α Piscis Austrini he described as 'the one in the mouth'. Ptolemy's work was translated into

Arabic several times between the late eighth and late ninth centuries AD and in translation the description became fam al-hūt, 'the mouth of the fish'. The westernized version of this description is Fomalhaut, the star's present name. Other examples of star names with a similar derivation are Achernar (α Eridani), Algenib (α Persei) and Algol (β Persei). Many of them now bear so little resemblance to their Arabic source that contemporary Arabic astronomers find it difficult to transpose the names into Arabic!

Other names are more truly Arabic. These are the ones that were used long before the introduction of the Greek astronomical traditions to Arabic science and include Adhara (ε Canis Majoris), Almach (γ Andromedae), Alphard (α Hydrae), Benetnasch (η Ursae Majoris) and Aldebaran, or more correctly al-dabarān (α Tauri), the 'follower' of the Pleiades.

There is a third group of stars with names which seem to reflect an Arabic origin. But these names are in fact the result of guesswork combined with a lack of consistency on the part of translators. They are Arabic-sounding names which have no origin in Arabic works. Lesath (λ Scorpii) does come from a true Arabic word, las'a ('stinging' by a scorpion), but it was not used in any Arabic text. It was first introduced in a European text in 1600. Other examples are Al Tais (δ Draconis), Azha (η Eridani), Alkalurops (μ Boötis), Betelgeuse (α Orionis), Sheliak (β Lyrae) and Thuban (α Draconis). Betelgeuse has had many variants, including Malgeuze, Bedalgeuze, Bet Elgeuze and Beteigeuze; these are all bad guesses at the original Arabic yad al-jawzā, the hand of al Jawzā, or Orion, although the source of these bad translations was Ptolemy's description 'the shoulder of Orion'! Our modern name comes from the Bedalgeuze version introduced by John of London in 1246. Today there are more than two hundred Arabic star names in common use, but even now you'll find some inconsistency in spelling and differing explanations of a name's derivation.

3 · Pinning down the Stars

When you are searching for something, whatever it is, it is useful to have some idea of where to look. The instructions you've been given may be 'on the table in the kitchen', or, on a larger scale, 'just past the chemist, before you reach the library'. If you ask the way you'll be told to look out for things you will recognize and you will use them to guide you to the object or place you're searching for. Should there be no familiar landmarks, as may be the case when you are in the desert or at sea, the place you want can be pin-pointed by using the latitude and longitude reference system. The globe of the Earth is divided by lines of latitude which tell you how far north and south you are from the Equator. Similarly, lines of longitude tell you how far east and west you are from the internationally agreed starting point of the Greenwich meridian, which is zero longitude. With this system it is easy to find any spot on Earth.

A similar system of guidelines is used for the objects in the sky. You'll soon become familiar with the system and the sky will turn from a confusion of bright stars to an ordered set of constellations which can be used as signposts to travel from one place in the sky to another.

When we look at the night sky all the stars appear to be at the same distance from Earth. As the Earth spins on its eastward daily cycle the stars all appear to move together in the opposite, westward direction. Imagine the Earth as a golf ball inside a beach ball. Standing on the golf ball what you see is the inside of the beach ball covered in stars. As the golf ball, i.e. the Earth, spins the stars would appear to move too,

although in fact the beach ball in which they are set actually remains still. The imaginary celestial sphere which helps us find our way about the sky is like the imaginary beach ball. The sphere appears to spin on an axis which goes through two points equivalent to the poles on Earth, the north celestial pole and the south celestial pole. The celestial equator rings the celestial sphere half-way between the two poles.

The view from Earth is dependent on three factors, the time of day, the season and where you are observing from. The daily rotation of the Earth takes approximately 24 hours during which time the Earth rotates through 360°. So for every hour of time the sky will appear to alter by 15° (360 ÷ 24). Similarly, the Earth takes one year to orbit the Sun and as it does so our view of the celestial sphere changes along with the seasons. As the Earth moves along its path the stars appear to rise about 4 minutes earlier, or 1° further west, each night. Over the months this will radically change the view from your observing site at a specific time of night. Compare what you can see from Greenwich on two dates. At 10 p.m. GMT in early October Pegasus is dominant in the southern sky, but at the same time of night in early February Pegasus can no longer be seen above the horizon and Orion is the dominant constellation. The stars are always 'in' the sky but only half are above the horizon at any one time. Pegasus does come above the horizon in early February but only during the hours of daylight. Then we cannot see the stars of Pegasus because the light of our local star, the Sun, is so bright that it obliterates their fainter light.

The stars you see depend on the time, the season and your position on Earth. These three diagrams show the potential view of the night sky from three different viewing points, $51\frac{1}{2}°$N, the Equator, and the North Pole. What you will actually see from each position will then depend on the season and the time.

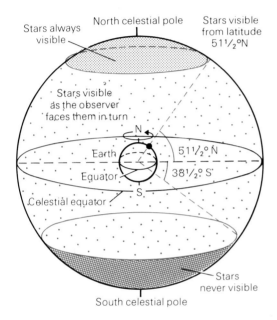

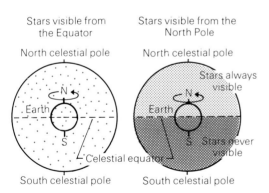

Stars visible from the Equator

Stars visible from the North Pole

The third factor which will affect your view is the place you are observing from. If you were to observe from the North Pole in the winter you'd certainly have a dark sky. There would be no street lights to interfere with your observing, but your viewing would be limited in another way. The north celestial pole would be directly overhead and the daily rotation of the Earth would mean that the stars would circle around the celestial pole without rising or setting. The stars in the southern half of the celestial sphere would never be visible. Should you wish to see just the southern stars the South Pole is the place for you. The star Polaris (α Ursae Minoris) is very close to the north celestial pole but, as we have seen, there is no star conveniently marking the southern pole. If you were to stand half-way between the two poles, on the Equator, what you'd see would be quite different. The celestial equator would be directly overhead, the north celestial pole would be on your northern horizon, and the southern to your south. You would be able to see all the stars on the celestial sphere during the course of a year. What is unusual is that all the star paths are perpendicular to the horizon.

It is most unlikely that you'll be observing from the poles, or perhaps even on the Equator, so what is the view going to be like from other locations on Earth? As you move south from the North Pole you will see not only a view of the northern stars, but also an increasing number of the southern stars. If you are travelling north from the South Pole you will see more and more northern stars as well as the southern ones. As you move north or south the position of the celestial pole appears to change. This position is directly related to your latitude. So, for someone at latitude $51\frac{1}{2}°$N, the latitude of London, the northern celestial pole is $51\frac{1}{2}°$ above the northern horizon. Similarly, at latitude 50°S the southern celestial pole is 50° above the southern horizon. In these two instances and at all other latitudes between the poles and the Equator, the stars

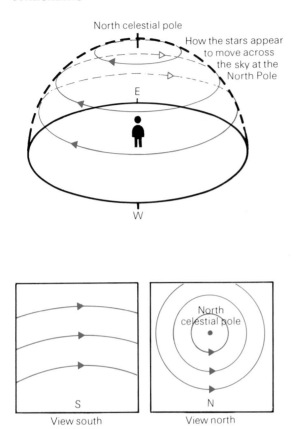

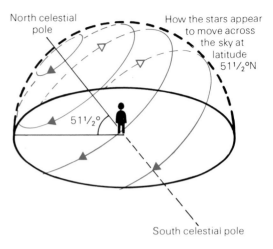

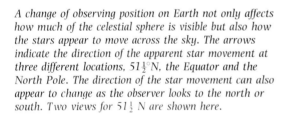

View south   View north

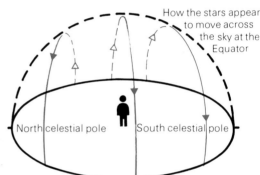

A change of observing position on Earth not only affects how much of the celestial sphere is visible but also how the stars appear to move across the sky. The arrows indicate the direction of the apparent star movement at three different locations, 51½°N, the Equator and the North Pole. The direction of the star movement can also appear to change as the observer looks to the north or south. Two views for 51½ N are shown here.

closest to the northern or southern pole appear to rotate around it without setting. These are known as the circumpolar stars. Of the remaining stars, one group will rise in the east and set in the west; the other is permanently below the horizon and never rises at all.

Thinking about the celestial sphere has helped us to identify what area of the sky we may see from one place on a certain time and date, but so far hasn't helped us to pinpoint a star or group of stars on that sphere. For this we need our network of reference lines. The co-ordinates that astronomers use which correspond to longitude and latitude are right ascension and declination,

RIGHT *The movement of the northern circumpolar stars as seen from the Northern Hemisphere Observatory on the Canary Islands. The short and bright star trail at upper right is Polaris.*

abbreviated to RA and Dec.

Declination is measured in degrees and parts of degrees to the north or south of the celestial equator. When declination is measured to the north it is given a positive value, when it is to the south the value is negative. The range of values is from $+90°$ at the north celestial pole, though $0°$ at the celestial equator, to $-90°$ at the south celestial pole. The degree is divided into 60 minutes of arc which are each divided into 60 seconds of arc. These units are abbreviated into deg. or $°$, arcmin or $'$, and arcsec or $''$.

Right ascension is measured eastwards along the celestial equator in hours, minutes and seconds. The measuring starts at the point where the path of the Sun crosses the celestial equator from south to north in March, the point known as the vernal equinox. This is also, more correctly,

called the First Point of Aries, which can be abbreviated to the symbol for the ram's horns (γ).

Here are some examples:

Star	Constellation	RA		Dec	
		hr.	min.	deg.	arc-min.
Capella α	Aurigae	05	16	+45	59
Sirius α	Canis Majoris	06	45	−16	42
Spica α	Virginis	13	25	−11	09
Vega α	Lyrae	18	36	+38	47

Although we regard the RA and Dec of an object as fixed they do change very slightly and very slowly. This is mainly because of the gravitational effects of the Sun and the Moon on the non-spherical Earth, as a result of which the Earth's axis describes a small circle in the sky over a long period of time, rather like the movement of a dying spinning top. This phenomenon is known as precession and is the reason why the First Point of Aries is no longer in the constellation of Aries but is now in Pisces. Precession can be detected only over relatively long periods and so charts and catalogues are drawn up for specific dates to be used for a certain period of time. These fixed dates are known as epochs and are quoted in the catalogues or atlases. Examples are 1900, 1950 and 2000. All the co-ordinates used in this book are for Epoch 2000. The other reason why RA and Dec change is because of the movement of the stars themselves. This has a much smaller effect and is much harder to detect. The movement has two components, one in the plane of the celestial sphere, i.e. across our line of sight, which is known as proper motion, and a second moving directly towards or away from us, which is known as radial velocity.

The system based on RA and Dec is known as the equatorial system. Another co-ordinate system, the horizon or altazimuth system, is mainly used for navigation, but is also useful to astronomers, particularly if you are trying to explain an object's position to a fellow observer.

A star's position is measured in right ascension (RA) and declination (Dec). The star in this diagram is Algol (β Persei) whose RA is 3 hrs 8 min. (angle X) and its Dec is 40° 57' (angle Y).

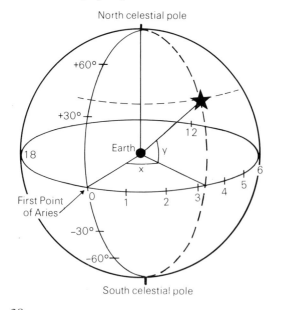

You specify the position of the object with respect to your (the observer's) horizon by reference to altitude and azimuth, which express the object's angle above the horizon and around it in relation to your meridian. Your meridian is a circle which runs through the north and south poles, through the point directly over your head, the zenith, and through the point directly below your feet, the nadir. As objects cross this line they are said to transit the meridian. An object reaches its greatest altitude above the horizon when it transits the observer's meridian; it is said to culminate at this point. Circumpolar stars cross the meridian twice, above and below the pole. These are upper culmination, which is the highest point a circumpolar star will reach in the sky, and lower culmination. An easy way of making rough angular measurements is by using your outstretched arm and hand—a fist is about 10°, a finger 1°, an outspread hand 22°. See the illustrations for guidance.

BELOW *Everyone can use their outstretched arm and hand to make angular measurements.*

Your body can be used to estimate the altitude (height) or azimuth (direction) of a star in relation to your surroundings.

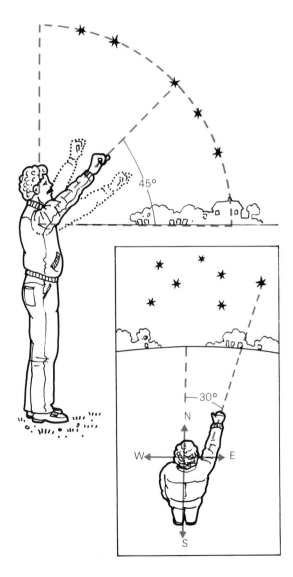

Star distances

The concept of the celestial sphere is useful in understanding how things appear, but it is not correct in one important respect because stars are not all the same distance away from us. Even stars within one constellation which seem to belong together can in reality be totally unrelated. It is our view from Earth which makes them appear close together and appear to move as if they were all on the surface of a large celestial sphere. Viewed from another angle it is easy to see how unrelated they are.

The distances between the stars are so vast that our units for measuring distances on Earth, the mile or the kilometre, prove to be totally inadequate. The unit often used to express these large distances in the universe is the light year (l.y.). Light travels faster than anything else, at a speed of 299,792 kilometres per second. A light year, or the distance a ray of light travels in one year, is equivalent to 9.46 million million kilometres. When the light year is used to express the distance between two stars it represents the time taken for light to cross that distance. Distances are measured from our local star, the Sun. Sirius is 8.8 l.y. and Betelgeuse 310 l.y. away from the Sun. When we are dealing with these vast distances it is quite proper to describe stars as being these distances away from us on Earth. After all, we are only 8.3 light minutes away from the Sun, a distance that disappears into insignificance even when we refer to the next nearest star, Proxima Centauri, some 4.3 l.y. away. Only fifty stars are closer than 15 l.y.; most are much more distant. For example, Polaris is 680 l.y. and Canopus 1200 l.y. from us.

Star distances are difficult to measure even when the stars are close. The first astronomer to have any real success in this field was Friedrich

The parallax method of calculating a star's distance involves measuring the star's position against the stellar background when the Earth is at A and again six months later from B. The star's apparent change in position against the background gives its parallax. This can be used to find the star's distance.

Bessel, who used the parallax method to measure star distances. This is based on the principle of observing your object from two different positions; if these are far enough apart the object will appear to shift against the more distant background, the angular measurement of the shift giving its distance. This same principle is used by surveyors to measure distances on Earth. Try it for yourself by observing a nearby prominent object against the backdrop of the far distance and see how it appears to move as you change your observing point.

Bessel observed the star 61 Cygni on two occasions six months apart. During that time the Earth had moved from one side of its orbit to the other. He was therefore observing the star from two positions 300 million kilometres apart, the diameter of the Earth's orbit. He found from the apparent movement of 61 Cygni against the background of other remoter stars that its angle of parallax was 0.3″ which gave a distance of 11 l.y. He was very close to the modern value of 11.1 l.y. The light year is a useful unit to use as it emphasizes the fact that distant objects are seen as they were when the light left them. We see Betelgeuse as it was 310 years ago and the light we receive from Sirius left that star 8.8 years ago.

The nearer the star is to us the greater the angle of parallax. Yet the angular measurements are still very small even when the star is comparatively close. Proxima Centauri has the greatest parallax shift of any star as it is closest to us, but even so this only amounts to the width of a small coin seen at a distance of 2 kilometres. With the much more distant stars astronomers estimate how far away they are by using their luminosity, and comparing the energy they emit with how bright they appear from Earth; although this is not so accurate, it is one of the very few methods available.

If a star had a *parallax* shift of exactly 1 *second* of arc it is said to be one *parsec* away. The parsec is also used to describe distances in astronomy and is sometimes used in preference to light years.

One parsec is equivalent to 3.26 l.y. The value of the parsec lies in the fact that the distance of a star in parsecs is equal to 1 ÷ angle of parallax. A star whose parallax is 0.1″ is 1 ÷ 0.1 = 10 parsecs away. Similarly a star whose parallax is 0.25″ is 1 ÷ 0.25 = 4 parsecs away. A larger unit, the kiloparsec (1000 parsecs) is also used.

The Sun has already been described as being 8.3 light minutes away from the Earth. Here we are using the unit devised for very large distances to describe a much shorter distance. It only takes 8.3 minutes for light to travel from the Sun to Earth, a distance of 149,597,870 kilometres.

Stars appear to be at equal distances from Earth, but this is only an illusion. The stars of the Plough in Ursa Major are shown here as they appear from Earth and at their true relative distances.

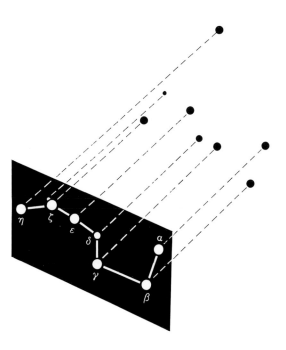

Astronomers refer to this distance as one astronomical unit (a.u.). The astronomical unit is used in relation to the Sun and the Sun's family of planets that make up the Solar System.

Star brightness

A star may appear brilliant because it is close to Earth or because it is very luminous, i.e. it is giving out energy at a great rate. Brightness is expressed in terms of magnitude. Apparent magnitude is how bright a star appears from Earth. A star's actual luminosity is related to its absolute magnitude.

It is the apparent magnitude of a star which is of most interest to the stargazer. This will give an indication of whether you can see the star from Earth. Hipparchus, one of Ancient Greece's most

The 21 brightest stars

(in order of increasing RA)

	Apparent magnitude	Absolute magnitude	Distance (l.y.)	Spectral type (see p. 33)
α Eridani (Achernar)	0.5	−1.6	85	B5
α Tauri (Aldebaran)	0.9	−0.3	68	K5
β Orionis (Rigel)	0.1	−7.1	900	B8
α Aurigae (Capella)	0.1	0.3	42	G8
α Orionis (Betelgeuse)	0.5	−5.6	300	M2
α Carinae (Canopus)	−0.7	−8.5	1200	F0
α Canis Majoris (Sirius)	−1.4	1.4	8.8	A1
α Canis Minoris (Procyon)	0.4	2.6	11.4	F5
β Geminorum (Pollux)	1.1	0.2	36	K0
α Leonis (Regulus)	1.4	−0.6	85	B7
α Crucis (Acrux)	0.9	−3.9	360	B1
β Crucis (Mimosa)	1.3	−5.0	420	B0
α Virginis (Spica)	1.0	−3.5	260	B1
β Centauri (Hadar)	0.6	−5.1	460	B1
α Boötis (Arcturus)	−0.1	−0.2	36	K2
α Centauri (Rigil Kentaurus)	−0.3	4.4	4.2	G2
α Scorpii (Antares)	1.0	−4.7	330	M1
α Lyrae (Vega)	0.0	0.5	26	A0
α Aquilae (Altair)	0.8	2.2	16.6	A7
α Cygni (Deneb)	1.3	−7.5	1800	A2
α Piscis Austrini (Fomalhaut)	1.2	2.0	22	A3

famous observational astronomers, classified the stars in terms of their brightness as long ago as the second century BC. He took the twenty brightest stars in the sky and described them as being of first importance, i.e. magnitude; the faintest stars normally visible to the unaided eye he described as being of sixth importance. The stars in between were given intermediate values. His 1 to 6 values of importance have now been converted into a numerical scale of apparent magnitudes. The larger the magnitude number the fainter the star. Celestial objects brighter than mag.1 have a zero or negative value. Those dimmer than mag.6 have a higher magnitude value. The faintest star so far detected with telescopes is at magnitude 24. The apparent magnitude of the Sun is -26.6 and the brightest object in the night sky, the full Moon, has a magnitude of -12.5. The planet Venus is -4.4 at its brightest. The brightest of the stars is Sirius at -1.46, Polaris is about $+2$.

The English astronomer Norman Pogson gave the magnitude scale a more formal scientific basis in the 1850s when he made the ratio between the brightness of a magnitude 1 star and a magnitude 6 star equal to exactly 100; that is, a difference of five magnitudes corresponds to a difference in brightness of a factor of 100. Thus stars of magnitude 6 are 2.512 times fainter than those of magnitude 5 and are 2.512×2.512 times fainter than a magnitude 4 star and so on.

Apparent magnitude bears no direct relationship to the star's actual light output. If all the stars were at the same distance then their apparent magnitudes would be true indicators of their luminosity, but they are not. The absolute magnitude of a star is related to how bright it would appear if it were moved to a standard distance of 10 parsecs (32.6 l.y.) from Earth. The figure is calculated from the star's apparent magnitude and distance. If the Sun was at a distance of 10 parsecs it would be a faint naked-eye star with a magnitude of $+4.7$. Sirius has an absolute magnitude of 1.4 and Polaris of -4.6.

Star colours

If you glance at the night sky you might think that the objects in it have no colour. But study the bright stars in the sky for a little longer and you will begin to notice their subtle colours. Take those in the shoulders of Orion, for example. Betelgeuse (α Orionis) is a bright, red star, whilst Bellatrix (γ Orionis) is a blue star. Close by is Sirius (α Canis Majoris), a brilliant white star. The individual colours are a direct result of the differing surface temperatures of the stars. The hottest stars are blue, with cooler stars appearing blue-white, white, yellow-white, orange and red as the temperature decreases. The coolest of all are the red stars.

The stars are classified into types according to their surface temperatures, which are revealed by analysing the light from the star. This is dispersed into a spectrum by a spectrograph, the astronomer's principal aid when studying starlight. The light from the star is spread out according to wavelength. Moving from long to short wavelength, a complete spectrum will give all the colours of the rainbow—red, orange, yellow, green, blue, indigo and violet. The temperature of the star's surface determines the distribution of light in the star's spectrum. Hotter stars emit more blue light than cooler stars, and conversely cooler stars emit more red light than hotter stars. The surface temperature could be anything from about 40,000°C to about 3000°C. The principal star types based on temperature are designated by one of the following letters: O, B, A, F, G, K, M. (You can remember this list by the sentence, 'Oh Be A Fine Girl Kiss Me'.) There are a few other rarer classes, but we can ignore these. Each class has ten main subdivisions, similarly related to temperature. These are numbered 0–9, hottest to coolest. The overall range in stars is from about 05 to M8.

The stars have colour but it isn't always that easy to see it and what you call red may be deep orange to another observer. Your own eyesight

Principal star types based on temperature

Type	Colour	Surface temperature range (°C)	Example
O	Blue	40,000–25,000	ζ Puppis
B	Blue	25,000–11,000	Spica (α Virginis); Rigel (β Orionis)
A	Blue-white	11,000–7500	Sirius (α Canis Majoris); Vega (α Lyrae); Deneb (α Cygni); Altair (α Aquilae)
F	White	7500–6000	Polaris (α Ursae Minoris); Procyon (α Canis Minoris); Canopus (α Carinae)
G	Yellow-white	6000–5000	Sun; Capella (α Aurigae)
K	Orange	5000–3500	Arcturus (α Boötis); Pollux (β Geminorum); Aldebaran (α Tauri)
M	Red	3500–3000	Betelgeuse (α Orionis); Antares (α Scorpii)

and viewing conditions will affect the colours you can see. At very low light the eye only images in black and white. Colours can be more easily seen when stars of contrasting colours are viewed together. A number of double stars (see Chapter 4) offer that opportunity, although you'll need a telescope to see the effect. But don't expect too much—even very experienced naked-eye observers are unable to classify stars into the OBAFGKM system by observing their colour.

LEFT *When the stars of Orion are photographically trailed across the sky their colours are revealed.*

Contrasting double stars

Name	Brighter star	Fainter star
η Cassiopeiae	Yellow	Purple
α Piscium	Pale green	Blue
γ Andromedae	Orange	Sea green
ι Cancri	Orange	Blue
ε Boötis	Pale orange	Sea green
ζ Coronae Borealis	White	Light purple
α Herculi	Orange	Emerald green
β Cygni	Yellow	Sapphire blue
α Cassiopeiae	Greenish	Bright blue

Star sizes and masses

One of the most important diagrams in astrophysics is the Hertzsprung-Russell diagram, known to most astronomers simply as the H-R

The Hertzsprung-Russell diagram relates a star's luminosity to its spectral type. Most stars, including our Sun, fall within the band known as the main sequence.

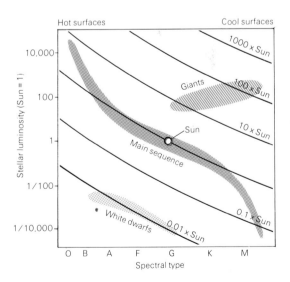

diagram. It is named after the two astronomers who first used it as a means of representing stellar characteristics. It is a graph which relates a star's luminosity (i.e. the rate of energy output) to its spectral type (i.e. surface temperature). If we plot all the bright stars on this diagram we find that they are not scattered all over the place but actually fall into two obvious bands. One moves from top left to bottom right and is known as the *main sequence*. Stars in this band include the Sun. The second group is made up of what are known as giants and these appear in the top right-hand part of the graph. The word 'giant' is used because they are much larger than main-sequence stars. There are a set of lines on the H-R diagram. Stars which fall on these lines have the same radii. The Sun, for example, has a radius of 700,000 kilometres and so do the other stars on the same line. But giant stars are a hundred to a thousand times larger. ε Aurigae, the largest known giant, is two thousand times bigger than the Sun, which means its diameter is larger than the orbit of Saturn! At the bottom left of the H-R diagram is a region known as the stellar graveyard. Towards the end of its life a star shrinks to become a white dwarf, a dead cinder of stellar material about as big as planet Earth. As you can see, there are many different types of star in the sky and each one is at a particular stage in its life cycle. The natural history of stars is a vast and complicated subject which is studied in more detail in another volume in this series.

Mass, the quantity of matter a body contains, is another important stellar characteristic, and you might think that it was directly related to a star's luminosity. Again the H-R diagram is very useful in showing us how the two are connected. Stars which are further up the main sequence than the Sun, i.e. more luminous and with hotter surfaces, turn out to be more massive. Conversely stars which are further down the main sequence than the Sun are less massive. The Sun has a mass of 2×10^{27} tonnes (10^{27} means 1 with 27 noughts after it!). The most massive star is about sixty times more massive than the Sun, the least massive only about 1/20 the solar mass. Stars of some masses are more numerous than others. In fact the *average* star is about 1/10 the mass of the Sun. What the diagram shows is that the luminosity of a main sequence star is *not* proportional to its mass but to mass$^{3.5}$, i.e. mass multiplied by itself 3.5 times.

4 · Double Stars

One of the great joys of observing is discovering for yourself that the heavens are not all they seem. If you glance upwards on a clear night, you will see a sky studded with pin-points of light. But some of these apparently single stars can be transformed into a pair when looked at through binoculars. Each member of the pair might itself be made up of two stars, and so on. These double stars are very common in our Galaxy and you can be rewarded time and time again when you turn your binoculars or telescope skyward. In fact only about half the stars in the sky are single, like our Sun; the rest are in pairs, or groups of three or four.

These pairs of stars often appear to be so close together that they look like a single star to the unaided eye. But the stars in a pair may be totally unrelated, in the same way as the groups of stars which make up constellations. Some of the doubles that we see from Earth are in fact separated by great distances; they just happen to fall together on our line of sight from Earth; these are called *optical doubles*. But by far the larger number of double stars are closely related pairs and companions in the true sense of the word. These are physical pairs, or *binaries*, although the term in common usage is double. It is not surprising that they are physically associated, since all stars originate in clusters. Our Sun once had about a thousand brothers and sisters all born from the same gas cloud. Over the last 5 thousand million years this cloud has decayed and lost stars.

By observing the motions of the two stars in a double it is possible to establish their relationship.

The movements of the stars forming an optical pair are unrelated, but in a true binary each star moves in an ellipse around the other. They travel round each other under their mutual gravitational attraction, each star orbiting the centre of their combined mass. Double stars that are far enough apart to be easily separated with the aid of a telescope are known as *visual doubles*. They have orbital periods ranging from about one year (actual separation about 2 a.u.) to thousands of years. The centres of the two stars have to be separated by at least 0.5 arcsecs for their orbits to be measured by telescopic means. If this can be done accurately the individual masses of the two stars can be calculated.

Ursa Major contains an interesting example of a double star. With keen eyesight, or better still binoculars, Mizar (ζ UMa, mag. 2.3) proves to have a companion, Alcor, of magnitude 4.0. These two stars are an optical pair. Closer investigation of Mizar will show it to be one of the stars in a true double as well. The first person to see Mizar's true companion was the Italian astronomer, Giambattista Riccioli, in around 1643. Towards the end of the nineteenth century it was shown that Mizar A, the brighter of the pair, is itself a binary. It was later found that Mizar B and Alcor also have companions. So the original star, Mizar (ζ UMa) has now been proved to be a multiple star. But don't expect to see all six components. A telescope will only be able to identify three; Mizar A, Mizar B and Alcor. Their individual components are *spectroscopic binaries*, binaries which can only be identified by analysing their starlight.

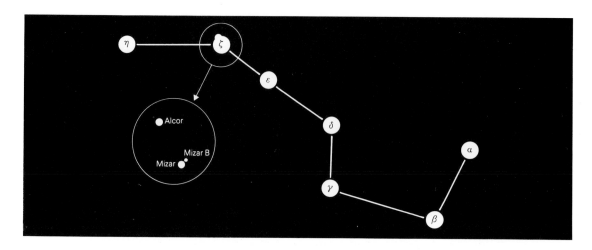

ABOVE *The stars of the Plough in Ursa Major include an interesting double star, one component of which is itself a double.*

BELOW *Mizar's companion Alcor is easily seen in this photograph of the Plough. The camera has also caught a meteor moving head on towards the observer. It is the spot at top centre above δ UMa, which could easily be mistaken for a star.*

Claudius Ptolemy first used the phrase 'double star' with reference to v_1 and v_2 Sagittarii. These two are in fact unrelated but appear close together as viewed from Earth. During the eighteenth century, after the discovery of many doubles, astronomers felt that some of these stars must be real companions and not optical doubles. The first observation that showed a double star to be a pair of stars with interrelated motions was

made by Sir William Herschel in 1803. The work of Félix Savary, twenty-four years later, heralded the start of research into binary stars. He showed that Mizar A and Mizar B were visual binaries orbiting in an ellipse over a sixty-year period.

At the end of the 1880s a new way of detecting doubles was discovered. Whilst studying the light from β Aurigae the astronomer Antonia Maury discovered that she was looking at the light spectrum from two stars and not just one. Each star has an individual spectrum which reveals its chemical composition, temperature and movement (see p. 33). In the case of a spectrosopic binary the two stars are often too close together to be seen as individuals even in large telescopes, but their presence can be detected by studying the spectrum of their combined light and noting

Corona Borealis, the Northern Crown, consists of an arc of seven stars. It is seen here at lower left, just above the rooftop. Gemma (α Coronae Borealis), the bright star marking the centre of the curve and appearing to almost rest on the roof, looks like a single star to the naked eye but closer investigation shows it to be an eclipsing binary of the Algol type.

periodic shifts in the positions of the spectrum lines. This was how Mizar A, Mizar B and Alcor were discovered to be spectroscopic binaries. The two stars in a binary will periodically move towards the observer and then away from him. This will be reflected in the star's light spectrum, which will register bluer when the star is moving towards us and redder when it is moving away.

As the two stars in a binary system revolve around each other one may partly or wholly obscure or eclipse the other depending on the view of the orbit from Earth. In an *eclipsing binary* the two stars are revolving around each other in a plane which is on or very close to the line of sight from Earth. The result is that they alternately eclipse each other. The degree of the eclipse will depend on how close the plane of the orbit is to the line of sight, and on the relative diameters of the stars. These double stars are detected by the periodic variation in the brightness of the stars. These variations in apparent magnitude were first observed by Geminiano Montanari when he was looking at Algol (β Persei) in 1670. The diminution in brightness is most noticeable when a brighter star is eclipsed by a fainter, and in this double one star is much brighter than its companion. In other systems the brightness of the two stars may be equal. More than four thousand eclipsing binary systems are now known. The period over which their brightness varies ranges from a few hours up to about ten days, although there are a few outside these limits. If the period is 12 hours the stars are on average 6 solar radii apart; a binary with a 10-day period has components separated by an average of 40 solar radii.

The stars known as *astrometric binaries* are another class of true doubles. By repeatedly measuring the positions of certain stars astronomers discovered irregularities in their slow movement across the celestial sphere indicating the presence of an invisible perturbing companion. Sirius (α Canis Majoris) belongs to this group. The primary star Sirius A is the brightest star in the sky with a magnitude of -1.4; Sirius B, its white dwarf companion (see p. 67), has a magnitude of 8.5. They orbit their common centre of mass every fifty years. The individual stars of some twenty known astrometric binary systems are not observable with even the very largest telescopes.

Double stars are among the easiest objects to find when stargazing. Many familiar constellations offer you double stars, and good examples are often key stars, i.e. bright signposts. You can start looking at doubles from your first night of stargazing. Each pair is different and as there are so many you have lots of nights of double stargazing ahead. As the stars in a pair are more difficult to resolve when they differ greatly in brightness, give yourself the best possible chance. Use your planisphere to pick doubles that will be high in the sky, as seeing is more difficult at low altitudes. Also, don't forget that separations and position angles change over the years, so make sure your information on positions is up to date. Several double stars are described in Chapter 7 but here are some for easy reference:

Doubles
(in order of increasing RA)

	Apparent magnitudes		Angular separation *(arcsecs)*
α Piscium	4.2	5.1	2.1
α Ursae Minoris	2.0	9.0	18.3
θ Eridani	3.4	4.5	8.2
α Tauri	0.9	13.4	30.4
β Orionis	0.1	6.8	9.5
λ Orionis	3.6	5.5	4.4
γ Leporis	3.7	6.3	94.0
σ Puppis	3.3	9.4	22.4
γ Velorum	1.9	4.2	41.2
γ Leonis	2.2	3.5	4.3
α Crucis	1.4	1.9	4.4
γ Crucis	1.6	6.7	110.6
ζ Ursae Majoris	2.3	4.0	14.4
ε Lyrae	4.7	4.5	207.7
Epsilon 1	5.0	6.1	2.6
Epsilon 2	5.2	5.5	2.3
β Cygni	3.1	5.1	34.4
δ Cygni	2.9	6.3	2.1
γ Delphini	4.5	5.5	9.6
61 Cygni	5.2	6.0	27.0

5 · Variable Stars

If you've got past the stage of simply gazing at the stars and want to feel more involved, try observing variable stars. These are the stars which change their brightness over a particular time period. We've already met a type of star that could be loosely regarded as a variable—the eclipsing binary. The variation in apparent brightness in this instance is due to one star eclipsing the other. In contrast, in the standard type of variable the luminosity of the star varies because of something directly connected with the star itself. This variability is usually due to changes or instabilities in the structure of the star leading to changes in its size and surface temperature. Very occasionally it may be caused by a rotating star whose surface temperature is not uniform. As the star turns, we are able to see regions of different temperature which are more or less luminous and so appear to shine more or less brightly. Whatever the reason, you'll have the excitement of watching the star appear to change from night to night.

Before you start this type of observing, you should have become familiar with at least one area of the sky and be able to distinguish differences in stellar magnitude. The change in the magnitude of the majority of variables is not large. You're not looking out for stars that change from, for example, mag. −1 to mag. 8, but there are plenty which offer a change of around two magnitudes. When you become very practised and are able to distinguish mag. 0.3 from 0.4, you can move on to the variables with the smaller magnitude changes, but even a practised observer can only estimate apparent magnitude to an accuracy of about 0.1 magnitude. As well as the expected magnitude difference, you also need to know the time period over which the change will happen. It could be hours, days or months, distinguishing short-period from long-period variables. You also need to know if the change is likely to follow a regular pattern or whether it will take a different form on each occasion. There are several types of variables and you need to know which group your star belongs to before you go out observing.

Possibly the easiest group to observe are those whose brightness varies in a regular cycle. The best known of this type are the *Cepheid variables* named after the first known member of this group, δ Cephei, discovered by John Goodricke in 1784. It has a period of 5.4 days and changes from mag. 3.5 to mag. 4.4. We now know of around seven hundred Cepheid stars in our Galaxy. Polaris (α Ursae Minoris) is an easy one for observers in the northern hemisphere to find, changing between mag. 1.9 and 2.1 over a four-day period. As a whole Cepheids vary over periods from around one to sixty days with a magnitude variation of between 0.5 and 1.

Cepheids are a particularly important group of stars because there is a relationship between their luminosities and their periods of variation. The period–luminosity relationship was discovered by the American astronomer Henrietta Leavitt in 1912 whilst studying Cepheids in the nearby galaxies known as the Magellanic Clouds. She found that the absolute magnitude of stars with longer periods was always greater than those with shorter periods. By measuring the time over which a Cepheid varies it is possible to obtain its absolute magnitude from the established period–luminosity relationship. The distance of the star can then be deduced by comparing this with its observed apparent magnitude. This is particularly useful because the Cepheids are very luminous and still observable at large distances and so can act as indicators of how far away related objects are. In the 1920s Edwin Hubble studied Cepheids in nearby spiral galaxies (see p. 47) and was able to show that these galaxies lie far beyond our own.

Other short-period variables include the *W Virginis* stars, found in globular clusters (see p. 50). These tend to be fainter than the Cepheids. The *RR Lyrae* stars, with periods of generally less than a day, are also cluster variables. Rather surprisingly these all have roughly equal luminosities. Long-period, or *Mira* stars, change over periods of thirty to one thousand days. Neither their period nor their range of magnitude is constant. In the case of Mira Ceti (*o* Ceti), the star which gives its name to this group, the period of variation fluctuates several days either side of eleven months and the star's magnitude can range from around 2 to around 10.

Semi-regular variables have small ranges of magnitude change and periods which are almost impossible to detect. The best known example of this group is Betelgeuse (α Orionis), a red giant. The irregular variables have no set periods at all. There are many other groups, including variables which have unforeseen and abrupt increases in brightness, but there are so many of the types already mentioned that they alone will give you more than enough material for observation.

Before setting out to observe your first

The constellations of Eridanus and Cetus. Mira Ceti, photographed near its maximum magnitude, is at centre right.

variables select examples which are appropriate to your viewing apparatus, whether it is the naked eye, binoculars or a telescope. Finding your star may well be the hardest part if you are over-ambitious to start with. As always, first consult your planisphere to see what is in the sky on that date at that particular time and location. Then plan how you will star-hop to your chosen star. Use stars of known magnitude nearby to compare the brightness. It is sometimes useful to look at stars out of focus when you are doing a comparison of magnitudes, as it is easier to compare the brightness of the large discs produced by an unfocused lens than to try and estimate the luminosity of pin-points. Finally, work out the magnitude of the variable for yourself. Wipe preconceived notions of what the magnitude ought to be from your mind. Keep a record of what you've observed and eventually you'll have a record over the whole cycle of variation.

Two special kinds of variables are the novae and supernovae. A *nova* is a star which flares up dramatically, usually over a few hours, and then returns to its original state. As the name implies this sudden change in brightness led the first observers to believe they were looking at a new star. Typical examples are T Coronae Borealis and RS Ophiuchi. T Coronae Borealis went nova in 1866 and 1946. Its brightness increased about 2500 times, the equivalent of a change in magnitude of 8.5. RS Ophiuchi increased in brightness 800 times in 1898, 1933 and 1958, equivalent to a change in magnitude of 7.3. The sudden increase in brightness is followed by a gradually steepening decline over a few months. Novae are very close binary stars. One of the pair is a hot compact body, a white dwarf. When material from the second star falls on the dwarf it ignites explosively, and some is blown away from the binary system at velocities of around 1000 kilometres per second. It is this nova outburst that can be observed from Earth.

Supernovae are much rarer than novae. A

Variables
(in order of increasing RA)

	Type and period	Magnitude range
β Persei	eclipsing binary 2.8 days	2.1/3.4
β Doradus	Cepheid 9.8 days	3.5/4.1
R Carinae	Mira 308.7 days	3.9/10.5
Z Ursae Majoris	semi-regular 196 days	7.9/10.8
R Crucis	Cepheid 5.8 days	6.4/7.2
R Centauri	Mira 546.2 days	5.3/11.8
δ Librae	eclipsing binary 2.3 days	4.9/5.9
RR Scorpii	Mira 279.4 days	5.0/12.4
RR Lyrae	RR Lyrae type 0.6 days	7.1/8.1
η Aquilae	Cepheid 7.2 days	3.9/4.4
δ Cephei	Cepheid 5.4 days	3.5/4.4
β Pegasi	irregular	2.3/2.7

supernova also flares up dramatically resulting in a massive increase in luminosity. But in this case the star literally blows up and ejects a large percentage of its mass into space. So far only three have been recorded in our Galaxy. The first, in 1054, was seen by the Chinese in the constellation of Taurus. At maximum, it was brighter than Venus and could be seen in full daylight. The remnants of this explosion are the Crab Nebula, M1, and a small compressed star known as a neutron star. The two other supernovae were in Cassiopeia in 1572 and in Ophiuchus in 1604. Much to astronomers'

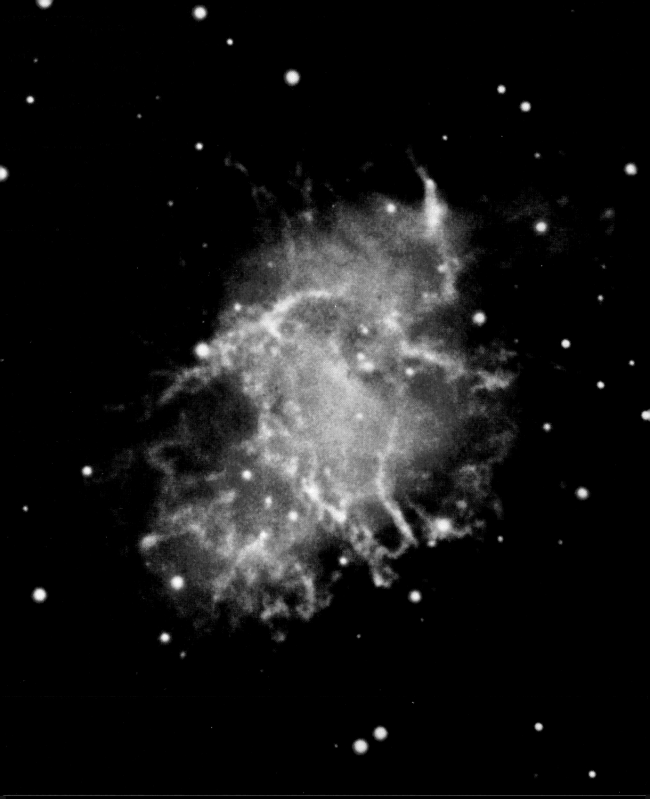

1987A
progenitor

1 arcmin

N
E

1 arc min

N
E

delight another supernova was observed in February 1987, this time in the Large Magellanic Cloud, a companion galaxy to our own Galaxy. Within two days it reached magnitude 4.4, which made it 10,000 times brighter than anything else within the Large Magellanic Cloud. On 22 February it was fainter than magnitude 12, on the 23rd it had reached magnitude 6 and on the

These two photographs show the startling appearance of a supernova. The photograph on the right was taken on 26 February 1987.

24th magnitude 4.4 was recorded. This recent sighting gave astronomers an unprecedented opportunity to study the development of a supernova. Every possible instrument was used to observe and record the event and every stargazer within sight of the Large Magellanic Cloud took advantage of this rare spectacle.

LEFT *The Crab Nebula (M1) in Taurus. It is the remains of the supernova star seen in 1054.*

45

6 · Deep Sky Objects

Deep sky objects lie beyond our stellar neighbourhood. These are the star clusters and galaxies which may themselves be made up of thousands of stars, and the clouds of gas known as nebulae. Although they are some of the dimmest objects in the sky, they are not beyond the observing capabilities of the beginner, but they do demand patience. With deep sky objects it is particularly important to let your eyes get used to the dark. Spend the first 15 to 20 minutes looking at stars before trying to find these remoter objects. Then use these brighter stars and constellations to find the hazy patch that may be a cluster, a nebula or a galaxy.

Your eye is most sensitive to a faint object when that object is not in your direct line of vision. Try looking at the sky just above the object, averting your gaze from what you want to see, and see how this helps. There will be some improvement in detectability, but you'll never be able to see the details and colours of these remote objects as so often depicted in long-exposure photographs. Averted vision is not the way to look for colour. The ability to see colour also varies from person to person. But in general the surface brightness of the object needs to be as great as that of the Orion Nebula (M42) in order to stimulate the relevant cells in the eye. Some people can see pastel reds in the Orion Nebula's brighter regions. Others have some success with the small and bright planetary nebula. Do not expect too much of any of these objects and you will not be disappointed.

Galaxies are systems containing enormous numbers of stars. Our local star, the Sun, and the other stars we see in the night sky belong to our own Galaxy. It contains around 100 thousand million stars. (This is more simply written as 10^{11}, '11' signifying the number of '0's; 10^1 is 10.) Other galaxies contain between 10^6 and 10^{12} stars. Our Galaxy is often called the Milky Way as it can be seen at night as a hazy river of milky light stretching across the darkened sky. The light comes from millions of stars which can only be seen individually with the aid of binoculars or a telescope.

The Origin of the Milky Way by Tintoretto. Jupiter holds the infant Hercules to the breast of the sleeping Juno. Some of the milk spilt upwards and formed the Milky Way and some more rained on to Earth and produced lilies.

The Milky Way seen from Australia in March 1986. Halley's Comet is in the centre of the photograph close to the horizon.

Our Galaxy is shaped like a disc with a central bulge and with arms of stars spiralling out from that centre. The Sun is situated way off centre, in one of the spiral arms. It is 32,000 l.y. from the centre of the Galaxy, approximately three-fifths of the way to the outside edge. If we look from Earth towards the edge of the Galaxy we see fewer stars than if we look towards the centre, so the concentration of stars does vary somewhat. The stars are particularly dense in the region of the constellation Sagittarius which marks the direction of the heart of the Galaxy. From Earth the disc of the Galaxy looks like a band of stars around the sky and it is this river of light which is the Milky Way. (Note that our Galaxy is always spelt with a capital G, whereas other galaxies are not.)

There are three basic types of galaxy. The spirals, like our own, are subdivided into normal and barred spirals and further classified according to the openness of the spiral arms and the size of the nucleus. Those known as ellipticals range from the spherical to the flattened, while a third group called the irregulars have no discernible structure. Galaxies themselves seem to be collected into groups. Our Galaxy belongs to a group of around thirty galaxies called the Local Group. The largest member of this group is the

Andromeda Galaxy (M31, NGC 224, 2.2 million l.y.), found in the constellation of the same name. It can just be seen with the naked eye as an elliptical hazy patch but powerful instruments will show that it is a spiral galaxy like ours. M33 (NGC 598), the galaxy in Triangulum, is also a member of our Local Group. The total light of this

The fuzzy patch in the centre of this star field is the Andromeda Galaxy.

galaxy is equal to apparent magnitude 5.7. It can be seen in binoculars but it is difficult to distinguish against faint foreground stars.

There are two small companion galaxies to our own Galaxy in the southern constellations of Dorado and Tucana. These are known as the Small and Large Magellanic Clouds after the explorer Ferdinand Magellan who first brought them to the notice of European astronomers. The Large Magellanic Cloud, in Dorado, is at a distance of 170,000 l.y. and contains 10^{10} stars. It covers an area twelve times the apparent size of the Moon. The Small Magellanic Cloud (NGC 292) is further away, at a distance of 200,000 l.y. Binoculars will reveal individual stars in the former and the latter as made up of star clusters.

The constellation of Virgo and its neighbour Coma Berenices contain other groups of galaxies. The galaxy cluster in Virgo is made up of about three thousand members and is about 65 million l.y. away. Some of the easiest areas to see are listed under the details for Virgo on p. 83 Another galaxy worth looking at is the spiral Whirlpool Galaxy (M51, NGC 5194) in Canes Venatici, which has a magnitude of 8.4. The irregular companion next to it has a magnitude of about 9.6. M51 also has the distinction of being the first galaxy to be observed as a spiral. The Earl of Rosse made this discovery in 1845 using his 72-inch reflector, at that time the largest telescope in the world. A pair of binoculars will show M51 as a fuzzy light patch and not, unfortunately, in all its glory, even though it is face on to us.

Like other astronomical objects, galaxies have become familiar through long-exposure photographs taken with high quality instruments. The back-garden stargazer will get a very different view, but it will be equally exciting. Make sure you get the best results possible by viewing in dark, clear skies. Choose low magnification for your instrument in order to get the greatest contrast between the galaxy and the star background.

Lying within the disc of our Galaxy are *star clusters*, known as *open*, loose or galactic star clusters. They each contain in the region of a few hundred to a few thousand stars. They cannot, however, be regarded as permanent groups. The group will only stay together whilst their mutual gravitational attraction is strong enough to resist disruptive forces. Open clusters don't have any definitive shape or structure so each can offer a truly unique picture to the observer. They are thought to have originated from gas clouds in which matter condensed to form stars. The members of one particular cluster can thus be regarded as being of more or less the same age. Most open clusters are relatively young.

The best known of these open clusters, the Pleiades and the Hyades, are found in the constellation Taurus. Both can be seen with the naked eye and are well within the capabilities of the novice observer. The Pleiades is the younger of the two groups, having formed within the last 50 million years. It contains a total of about 100 stars, but seven, termed the 'seven sisters', are particularly dominant. These seven and many others are easily seen through binoculars, but the average unaided eye can only pick out five or six 'sisters'. Stars of the older Hyades were formed about 500 million years ago; they make the distinctive 'V' shape marking the head of the bull. Another open cluster for northern hemisphere observers is Praesepe in Cancer, also known as the Beehive and visible to the naked eye.

For southern observers the cluster known as the Jewel Box, κ Crucis, cannot be surpassed. It was named in the nineteenth century by John Herschel, who thought its stars of various colours looked like multicoloured jewellery. Another beautiful open cluster for observers in northern latitudes is the curiously named 'wild duck' in Scutum (M11, NGC 6705). The nineteenth-century astronomer W. H. Smyth who named it thought its fan-shape resembled wild ducks. It is best seen through a telescope, although binoculars will show its two hundred stars as a hazy patch. There are many more open clusters worth looking at out of the thousand or so now known. Some other good examples are listed under their parent constellation in Chapter 7.

The distinctive 'V' shape of the Hyades star cluster and six of the seven bright stars of the Pleiades cluster.

In contrast to the open cluster, the *globular cluster* is spherical and symmetrical. It also contains more stars and may have anything from a few tens of thousands to over a million, all moving within a relatively small volume of space. These clusters are more distant than the open clusters and their stars are nearly as old as the Galaxy itself. They are distributed in a roughly spherical halo around the central nucleus of our Galaxy and so we can see them in areas of sky away from the plane of the Milky Way. The constellation Ara contains the nearest, NGC 6397, more than 8000 l.y. away. The brightest

are in the southern hemisphere and we know of about a hundred altogether.

The finest globular cluster is Omega Centauri (ω Cen, NGC 5139). At a distance of 16,000 l.y., it is relatively close to us and is easily visible to the naked eye, covering an area of sky two-thirds the size of that occupied by the full Moon. Another fine example is 47 Tucanae (NGC 104, 19,000 l.y.), which is also visible to the naked eye. Its fuzzy starlike appearance will resolve into individual stars with a small telescope. The best globular cluster in the northern sky is in the constellation Hercules (M13, NGC 6205). It can be seen with the unaided eye, but you can only be sure by using binoculars. It is 22,500 l.y. away and contains around 300,000 stars.

Nebulae are clouds of gas and dust which can be visible as a bright or a dark patch against the star background. Some, such as the Orion Nebula, emit light of their own; others shine by reflection, as in the case of the nebulosity surrounding the brighter stars in the Pleiades cluster. The Orion Nebula (M42, NGC 1976, 1300 l.y.) is visible to the naked eye as a hazy patch of light, but reveals more through binoculars or a telescope. When a nebula is not illuminated, it is its lack of light which makes it visible. The gas cloud cuts out the light of the stars behind it and so appears as a dark patch in the sky. The easiest dark nebula to see is the Coal Sack in Crux, which stands out against the Milky Way.

The stars of tomorrow are born from the gas and dust of these nebulae, but a different type of nebula can also be associated with stars towards the end of their life cycle. A planetary nebula is a compact, round region of nebulosity which has been expelled from the star at its centre. These nebulae were named by Sir William Herschel in the late eighteenth century, who thought their appearance was similar to a planet's, but they have nothing to do with planets. The closest of all the planetary nebulae is in Aquarius. It is commonly known as the Helix Nebula (NGC 7293, 690 l.y.), and covers an area of the sky equal to about half the size of the Moon. However, although it appears large it is also quite faint and needs binoculars. The Dumbbell Nebula (M27, NGC 6853, 1250 l.y.) in Vulpecula is slightly

The Orion Nebula photographed through an $8\frac{1}{2}$ inch reflecting telescope.

smaller in apparent size, about a quarter of the area of the Moon, but brighter. A third planetary nebula to try is the Ring Nebula in Lyra (M57, NGC 6720, 4100 l.y.). Only larger telescopes will reveal its central hole.

Deep sky objects

Number	Constellation	Type	Apparent magnitude
M1	Taurus	Nebula	8.4
M13	Hercules	Globular cluster	5.9
M31	Andromeda	Spiral galaxy	3.4
M42	Orion	Nebula	4.0
M45	Taurus	Open cluster	1.2
M49	Virgo	Elliptical galaxy	8.4
M57	Lyra	Planetary nebula	9.0

7 · The View from Earth

This chapter gives you the sky and star information you need to go observing. The maps at the beginning of the chapter give you a complete view of the night sky for each season, whether you are in the northern or the southern hemisphere. Simply find the map to suit your location, direction of view and season, and start stargazing. There are two views for each season and location; one for an observer facing the northern horizon and a second for that same observer showing what he would see if he looked in the opposite direction, i.e. faced south rather than north. Together they cover the whole sky for the stated time and hemisphere. The maps have been drawn for observers situated at latitude 45°N or 35°S, but they can be easily used by people living at other latitudes. The star patterns will be the same, only their height above the horizon will alter.

For northern hemisphere observers living north of 45°N, the stars to the north will appear higher in the sky, and those to the south lower in the sky, by an amount equal to the difference in latitude. For example, if you live in London, Cardiff, or anywhere else with a latitude of $51\frac{1}{2}°$N, the stars to the north will appear $6\frac{1}{2}°$ higher and those to the south $6\frac{1}{2}°$ lower than shown on these maps. If your latitude is less than 45°N then the opposite is the case. For southern observers with a latitude greater than 35°S, the stars to the north will appear lower in the sky, and the stars to the south higher. Again the difference involved will be equal to the difference in latitude, and if the latitude is less than 35°S then the opposite is the case. Only the brightest of stars have been

included in these charts. These are the ones that will stand out and are used as stepping-stones across the sky. In general the maps include stars whose magnitude is classified as 1, 2 or 3, although there are some exceptions to this rule. The brighter the star, the larger the circle by which it is shown. Key stars are also marked. (See the key opposite.)

These maps are flat, compressing a hemisphere of information on to two half circles. They show an entire horizon in front of you, whereas in reality it extends all the way around your head. The distance from the horizon to the point over your head is also presented here on a flat surface. You can see this large expanse of sky on the maps without moving your head—your eye only needs to scan from the word 'north' to 'overhead', or from 'south' to 'overhead'. To cover the same area of sky outside involves much craning of the neck and moving of the head. Maps do have their limitations. If you bear these points in mind, or even practice finding stars by holding the map in front of you and moving it around to face different locations in the sky, you'll find what you are looking for more easily.

After the seasonal views, the highlights of some constellations are looked at in detail, with maps to show you where objects are. The two sets of maps are complementary and can be used together or individually. The constellations are good stopping places for your tour of the night sky and are given here in alphabetical order. Their highlights include deep sky objects such as nebulae, star clusters and galaxies, as well as single, double and variable stars. As throughout the book, stars are identified by their individual names if they have one. Otherwise they are given their accepted designation, usually a letter of the Greek alphabet. A similar policy is also adopted for the other objects; their proper name is given first, if there is one, and then their Messier or NGC number. These constellation maps include fainter objects than those on the seasonal maps. Many are within the limits of the naked eye, but others will require binoculars or a telescope and this is indicated where necessary. The distance of objects from Earth is also included.

The magnitude scales used are as follows:

Seasonal maps
Magnitude 2.6–3.5 •   Brighter than 1.5 ●
Magnitude 1.6–2.5 •   Key stars ◉

Constellation maps
Magnitude 4.6–5.5 •   Magnitude 1.6–2.5 ●
Magnitude 3.6–4.5 •   Brighter than 1.6 ●
Magnitude 2.6–3.5 ●   Key stars ◉

In addition, the constellation maps also include other deep sky objects and these are shown as follows:

Open star cluster ◯   Planetary nebula -◇-

Globular star cluster ◯   Galaxy ◯ ◦

Diffuse nebula ◠ ▫

Orion and Taurus in the night sky.

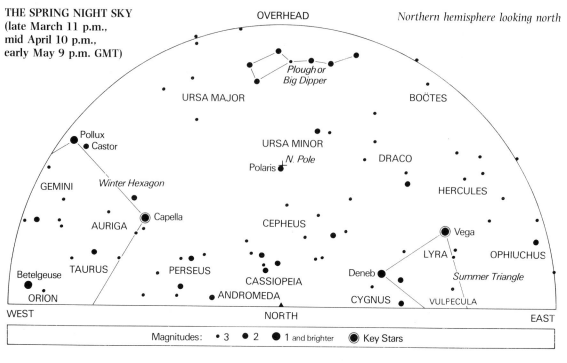

THE SPRING NIGHT SKY
(late March 11 p.m.,
mid April 10 p.m.,
early May 9 p.m. GMT)

OVERHEAD

Northern hemisphere looking north

*Plough or
Big Dipper*

URSA MAJOR

BOÖTES

Pollux
Castor

URSA MINOR

DRACO

GEMINI

Winter Hexagon

Polaris *N. Pole*

HERCULES

Capella

CEPHEUS

Vega

AURIGA

LYRA

OPHIUCHUS

TAURUS

PERSEUS

Deneb

Summer Triangle

Betelgeuse

CASSIOPEIA

CYGNUS

VULPECULA

ORION

ANDROMEDA

WEST

NORTH

EAST

Magnitudes: • 3 ● 2 ● 1 and brighter   ◉ Key Stars

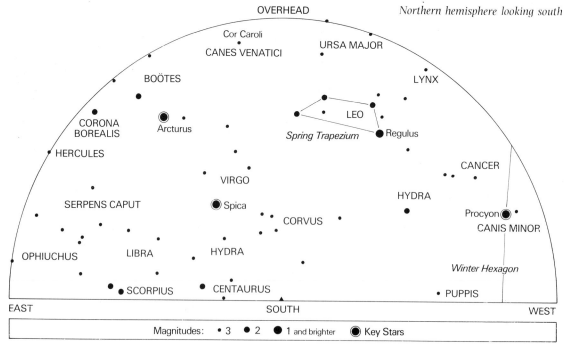

OVERHEAD

Northern hemisphere looking south

Cor Caroli

URSA MAJOR

CANES VENATICI

BOÖTES

LYNX

LEO

CORONA
BOREALIS

Arcturus

Regulus

Spring Trapezium

HERCULES

CANCER

VIRGO

HYDRA

SERPENS CAPUT

Spica

Procyon

CORVUS

CANIS MINOR

OPHIUCHUS

LIBRA

HYDRA

Winter Hexagon

SCORPIUS

CENTAURUS

PUPPIS

EAST

SOUTH

WEST

Magnitudes: • 3 ● 2 ● 1 and brighter   ◉ Key Stars

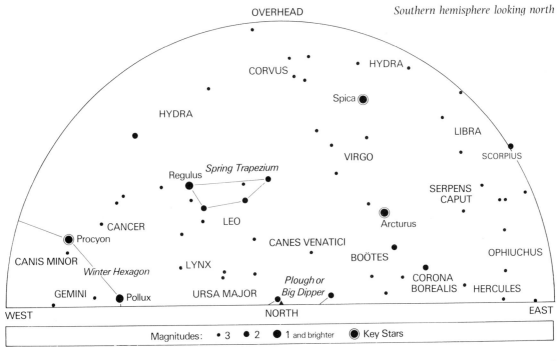

OVERHEAD

HYDRA

CORVUS

Spica

HYDRA

LIBRA

SCORPIUS

VIRGO

Regulus *Spring Trapezium*

SERPENS
CAPUT

Arcturus

LEO

CANCER

CANES VENATICI

BOÖTES

OPHIUCHUS

Procyon

CANIS MINOR

Winter Hexagon

LYNX

CORONA
BOREALIS

HERCULES

GEMINI

Pollux

URSA MAJOR

*Plough or
Big Dipper*

WEST

NORTH

EAST

Magnitudes: • 3 ● 2 ⬤ 1 and brighter ◉ Key Stars

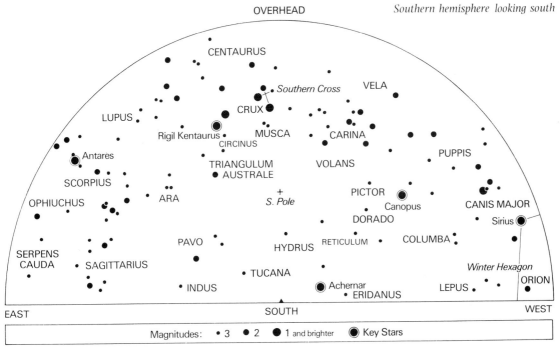

OVERHEAD

CENTAURUS

VELA

Southern Cross

CRUX

LUPUS

CARINA

Rigil Kentaurus

MUSCA

CIRCINUS

PUPPIS

VOLANS

Antares

TRIANGULUM
AUSTRALE

SCORPIUS

PICTOR

+ *S. Pole*

Canopus

CANIS MAJOR

ARA

OPHIUCHUS

DORADO

Sirius

PAVO

RETICULUM

COLUMBA

SERPENS
CAUDA

HYDRUS

Winter Hexagon

SAGITTARIUS

TUCANA

Achernar

LEPUS

ORION

INDUS

ERIDANUS

EAST

SOUTH

WEST

Magnitudes: • 3 ● 2 ⬤ 1 and brighter ◉ Key Stars

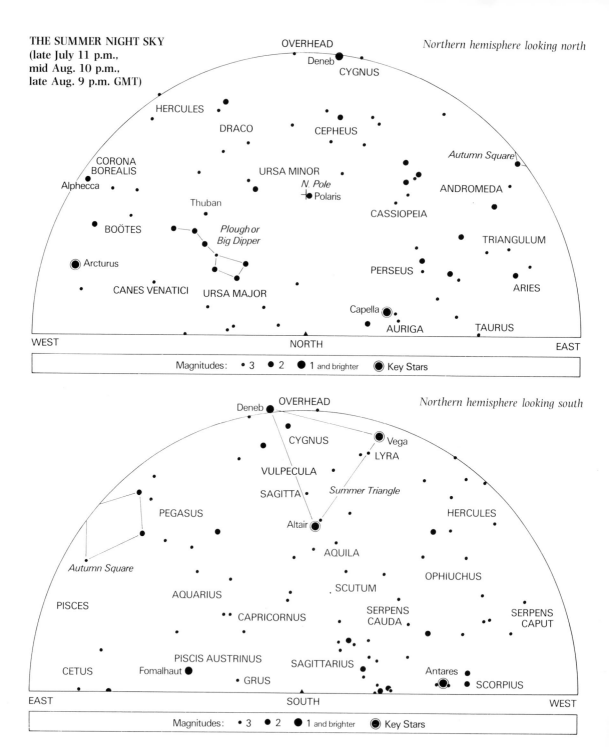

THE SUMMER NIGHT SKY
(late July 11 p.m.,
mid Aug. 10 p.m.,
late Aug. 9 p.m. GMT)

Northern hemisphere looking north

OVERHEAD

Deneb

CYGNUS

HERCULES

DRACO

CEPHEUS

CORONA
BOREALIS

Autumn Square

Alphecca

URSA MINOR

N. Pole

ANDROMEDA

Thuban

+ Polaris

CASSIOPEIA

BOÖTES

*Plough or
Big Dipper*

TRIANGULUM

Arcturus

PERSEUS

ARIES

CANES VENATICI

URSA MAJOR

Capella

TAURUS

AURIGA

WEST

NORTH

EAST

Magnitudes: • 3 ● 2 ⬤ 1 and brighter ◉ Key Stars

Deneb OVERHEAD

Northern hemisphere looking south

CYGNUS

Vega

LYRA

VULPECULA

SAGITTA

Summer Triangle

PEGASUS

Altair

HERCULES

AQUILA

Autumn Square

OPHIUCHUS

AQUARIUS

SCUTUM

PISCES

CAPRICORNUS

SERPENS
CAUDA

SERPENS
CAPUT

PISCIS AUSTRINUS

SAGITTARIUS

Antares

CETUS

Fomalhaut

• GRUS

SCORPIUS

EAST

SOUTH

WEST

Magnitudes: • 3 ● 2 ⬤ 1 and brighter ◉ Key Stars

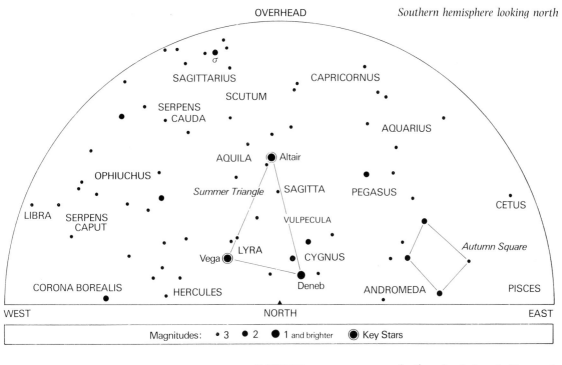

OVERHEAD

Southern hemisphere looking north

SAGITTARIUS
σ

CAPRICORNUS

SCUTUM

SERPENS
CAUDA

AQUARIUS

AQUILA · Altair

OPHIUCHUS

Summer Triangle SAGITTA

PEGASUS

CETUS

VULPECULA

LIBRA

SERPENS
CAPUT

LYRA

Vega

CYGNUS

Autumn Square

CORONA BOREALIS

HERCULES

Deneb

ANDROMEDA

PISCES

WEST   NORTH   EAST

Magnitudes: • 3 ● 2 ● 1 and brighter ◉ Key Stars

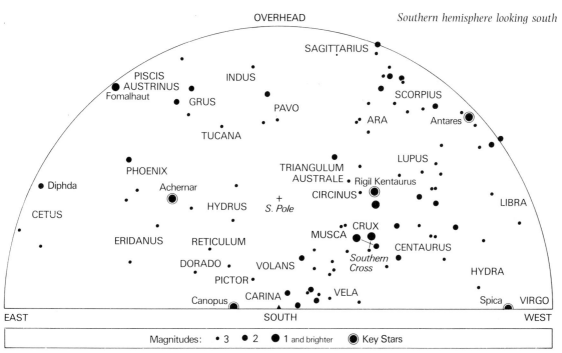

OVERHEAD

Southern hemisphere looking south

SAGITTARIUS

PISCIS
AUSTRINUS

INDUS

Fomalhaut

GRUS

SCORPIUS

PAVO

ARA

Antares

TUCANA

LUPUS

· Diphda

PHOENIX

TRIANGULUM
AUSTRALE · Rigil Kentaurus

Achernar

CIRCINUS

CETUS

HYDRUS

+
S. Pole

LIBRA

ERIDANUS

RETICULUM

MUSCA

CRUX

CENTAURUS

DORADO

VOLANS

*Southern
Cross*

HYDRA

PICTOR

Canopus

CARINA

VELA

Spica VIRGO

EAST   SOUTH   WEST

Magnitudes: • 3 ● 2 ● 1 and brighter ◉ Key Stars

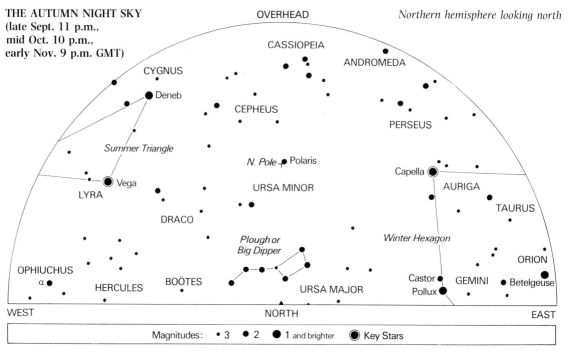

THE AUTUMN NIGHT SKY
(late Sept. 11 p.m.,
mid Oct. 10 p.m.,
early Nov. 9 p.m. GMT)

Northern hemisphere looking north

OVERHEAD

CASSIOPEIA

ANDROMEDA

CYGNUS

Deneb

CEPHEUS

PERSEUS

Summer Triangle

N. Pole Polaris

Capella

AURIGA

Vega

LYRA

URSA MINOR

TAURUS

DRACO

Winter Hexagon

ORION

*Plough or
Big Dipper*

Castor

GEMINI

Betelgeuse

OPHIUCHUS

α

HERCULES

BOÖTES

URSA MAJOR

Pollux

WEST

NORTH

EAST

Magnitudes: • 3 • 2 ● 1 and brighter ◉ Key Stars

OVERHEAD

Northern hemisphere looking south

ANDROMEDA

β

TRIANGULUM

PEGASUS

CYGNUS

ARIES

VULPECULA

PISCES

Autumn Square

Summer Triangle

SAGITTA

TAURUS

Aldebaran

CETUS

AQUARIUS

Altair

Winter Hexagon

AQUILA

ORION

ERIDANUS

Fomalhaut

CAPRICORNUS

SCUTUM

SERPENS
CAUDA

Rigel

PHOENIX

PISCIS AUSTRINUS

GRUS

EAST

SOUTH

WEST

Magnitudes: • 3 • 2 ● 1 and brighter ◉ Key Stars

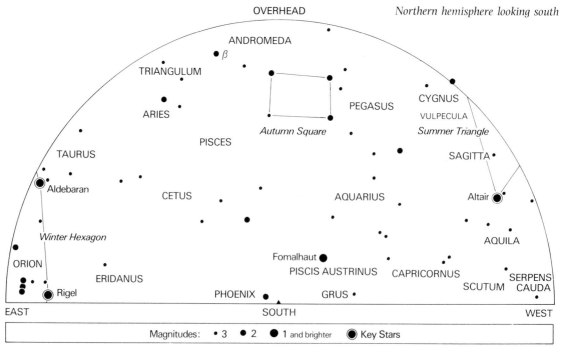

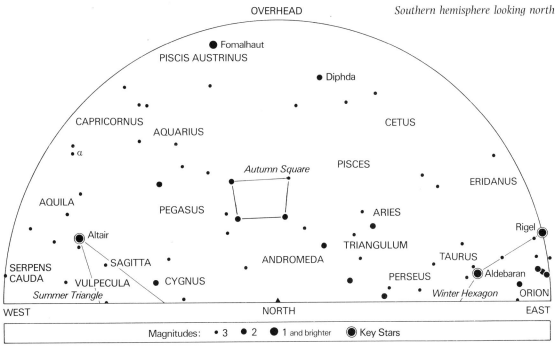

Southern hemisphere looking north

OVERHEAD

Fomalhaut
PISCIS AUSTRINUS

Diphda

CAPRICORNUS
AQUARIUS
CETUS

α

PISCES
ERIDANUS

AQUILA
PEGASUS

Autumn Square

ARIES

Rigel

Altair
TRIANGULUM
TAURUS

SAGITTA
ANDROMEDA
Aldebaran

SERPENS
CAUDA
VULPECULA
CYGNUS
PERSEUS
Winter Hexagon
ORION

Summer Triangle

WEST
NORTH
EAST

Magnitudes: • 3 ● 2 ● 1 and brighter ◉ Key Stars

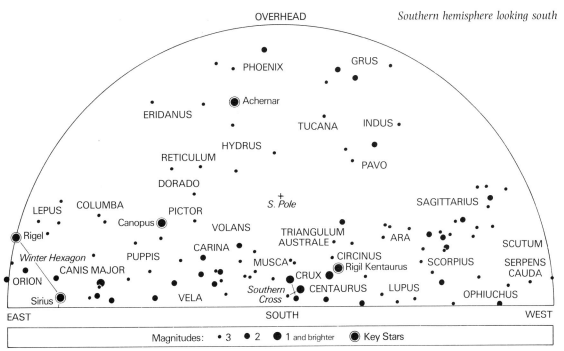

Southern hemisphere looking south

OVERHEAD

PHOENIX
GRUS

Achernar

ERIDANUS
TUCANA
INDUS

HYDRUS

RETICULUM
PAVO

DORADO

+
S. Pole

LEPUS
COLUMBA
PICTOR
SAGITTARIUS

Canopus
VOLANS

Rigel
CARINA
TRIANGULUM
AUSTRALE
ARA

Winter Hexagon
PUPPIS
MUSCA
CIRCINUS
SCUTUM

ORION
CANIS MAJOR
CRUX
Rigil Kentaurus
SCORPIUS
SERPENS
CAUDA

Sirius
VELA
*Southern
Cross*
CENTAURUS
LUPUS
OPHIUCHUS

EAST
SOUTH
WEST

Magnitudes: • 3 ● 2 ● 1 and brighter ◉ Key Stars

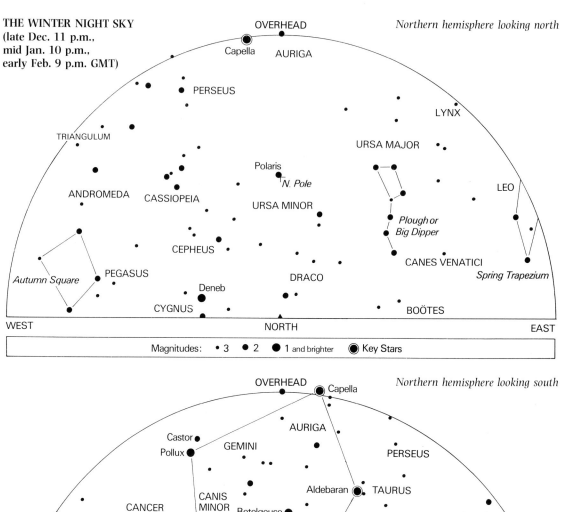

THE WINTER NIGHT SKY
(late Dec. 11 p.m.,
mid Jan. 10 p.m.,
early Feb. 9 p.m. GMT)

Northern hemisphere looking north

OVERHEAD

Capella

AURIGA

PERSEUS

LYNX

TRIANGULUM

URSA MAJOR

Polaris

N. Pole

LEO

ANDROMEDA

CASSIOPEIA

URSA MINOR

*Plough or
Big Dipper*

CEPHEUS

CANES VENATICI

Autumn Square   PEGASUS

Deneb

DRACO

Spring Trapezium

CYGNUS

BOÖTES

WEST

NORTH

EAST

Magnitudes: • 3 ● 2 ⬤ 1 and brighter ◎ Key Stars

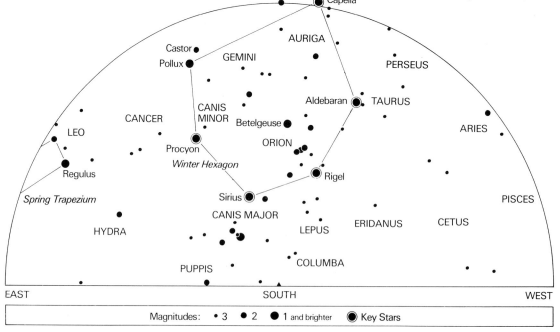

Northern hemisphere looking south

OVERHEAD   Capella

AURIGA

Castor

GEMINI

PERSEUS

Pollux

Aldebaran   TAURUS

CANCER

CANIS
MINOR

Betelgeuse

ARIES

LEO

Procyon

ORION

Winter Hexagon

Rigel

Regulus

Sirius

PISCES

Spring Trapezium

CANIS MAJOR

LEPUS

ERIDANUS

CETUS

HYDRA

PUPPIS

COLUMBA

EAST

SOUTH

WEST

Magnitudes: • 3 ● 2 ⬤ 1 and brighter ◎ Key Stars

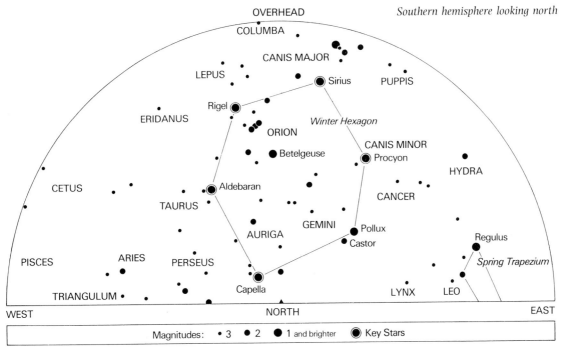

OVERHEAD

COLUMBA

CANIS MAJOR

LEPUS

Sirius

PUPPIS

Rigel

ERIDANUS

ORION

Winter Hexagon

CANIS MINOR

Betelgeuse

Procyon

HYDRA

CETUS

Aldebaran

TAURUS

CANCER

GEMINI

AURIGA

Pollux

Castor

Regulus

PISCES

ARIES

PERSEUS

Spring Trapezium

TRIANGULUM

Capella

LYNX

LEO

WEST

NORTH

EAST

Magnitudes: • 3 ● 2 ⬤ 1 and brighter ◉ Key Stars

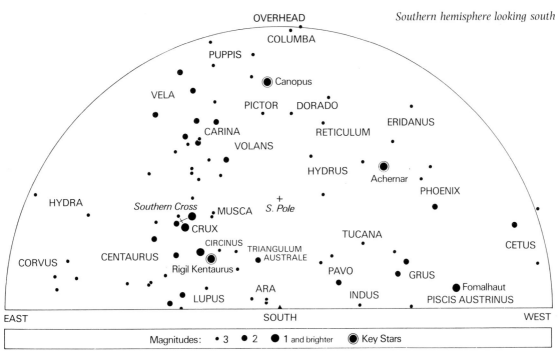

OVERHEAD

COLUMBA

PUPPIS

Canopus

VELA

PICTOR

DORADO

ERIDANUS

CARINA

RETICULUM

VOLANS

HYDRUS

Achernar

PHOENIX

HYDRA

Southern Cross

MUSCA

+ *S. Pole*

CRUX

CIRCINUS

TRIANGULUM
AUSTRALE

TUCANA

CETUS

CORVUS

CENTAURUS

Rigil Kentaurus

PAVO

GRUS

LUPUS

ARA

INDUS

Fomalhaut

PISCIS AUSTRINUS

EAST

SOUTH

WEST

Magnitudes: • 3 ● 2 ⬤ 1 and brighter ◉ Key Stars

The southern sky from Australia in February. The two bright stars at top left are χ and β Centauri. At lower right is the naked-eye nebula in the constellation of Carina, NGC 3372, which surrounds the variable star η Carinae. Crux lies in the centre of the photograph.

Andromeda

The stars in this constellation form the figure of Andromeda chained to a rock as a sacrifice. There are some interesting objects within the constellation but they do not form an obvious grouping. Andromeda is most easily found by the square of stars which includes Alpheratz (α, mag. 2.1, 70 l.y.). The three other stars are in the neighbouring constellation of Pegasus. Together they make up the Square of Pegasus, which is sometimes called the Autumn Square because it appears at this season in the northern hemisphere. Mirach (β, mag. 2.1, 88 l.y.) is a red giant. Almach (γ, 120 l.y.) is a good double star for a small telescope, with components of magnitude 2.2 and 5.0. π (390 l.y.) is another small telescope double, with stars of magnitude 4.4 and 8.6. Do not leave Andromeda without looking at the Andromeda Galaxy, M31 (NGC 224, 2.2 million l.y.). This is a spiral galaxy like our own and is the most distant object visible to the naked eye. Looked at without an instrument it appears as a hazy patch of light, but binoculars will improve the view considerably. It has two satellite galaxies nearby. You'll be able to pick out the brighter of the two, M32 (NGC

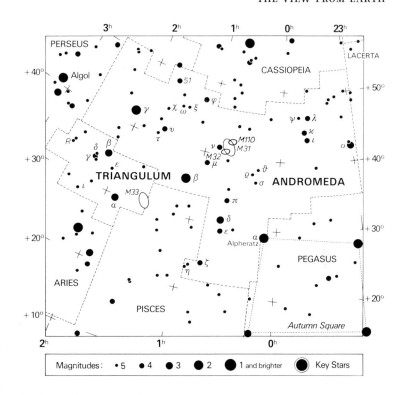

Magnitudes: • 5 ● 4 ● 3 ● 2 ● 1 and brighter ◉ Key Stars

221), with a small telescope. The second, M110 (NGC 205), is fainter and can be mistaken for a star.

Aquarius
The Water Carrier

Although the name of this constellation is familiar, its stars are not easily identified in the sky. The easiest ones to find are those near the border with Pegasus that make up the jug of the water carrier. They are centred around ζ (90 l.y.), which is a binary of 4.3 and 4.5 magnitude stars, but this will look like one star unless you have a sufficiently powerful telescope. Sadalmelik (α, mag. 3.0, 950 l.y.) and nearby Sadalsuud (β, mag. 2.9, 980 l.y.) are both yellow supergiants. Globular cluster M2 (NGC 7089, 37,000 l.y.) is visible in binoculars, but NGC 7009 (3000 l.y.), the planetary nebula known as the Saturn Nebula, needs a telescope. The nearest planetary nebula to the Sun, NGC 7293 (330 l.y.), known as the Helix Nebula, can be found with binoculars but it does appear faint.

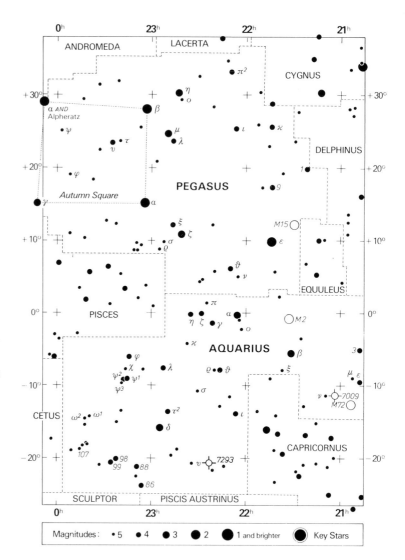

Aquila
The Eagle

Aquila is in the Milky Way and contains the bright and relatively close star Altair (α, mag. 0.8, 17 l.y.). Together with Deneb (α Cygni) and Vega (α Lyrae), Altair forms the triangle of stars which dominates the overhead sky until the winter months and for this reason is known as the Summer Triangle. Close to Altair are Alshain (β, mag. 3.7, 36 l.y.) and Tarazed (γ, mag. 2.7, 280 l.y.). Regular observations of η (1400 l.y.) will show that this is a variable star ranging from mag. 3.5 to 4.4 in a little over seven days.

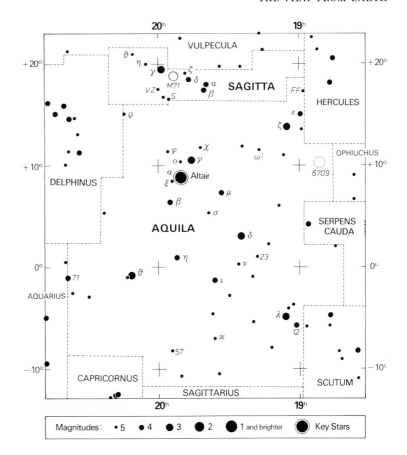

Magnitudes: • 5 ● 4 ● 3 ● 2 ● 1 and brighter ◯ Key Stars

Auriga
The Charioteer

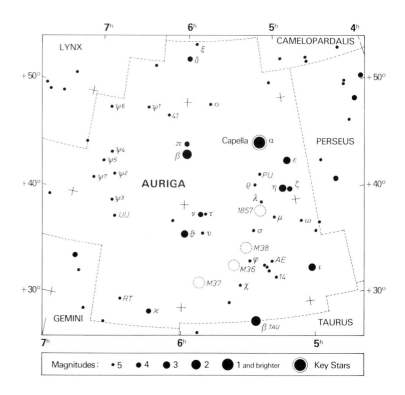

This constellation contains one of the brightest stars for observers in the northern hemisphere. It is the yellow star Capella (α, 42 l.y.), which has a magnitude of 0.1. Another bright star, Menkalinan (β, mag. 1.9, 72 l.y.), is, in fact, an eclipsing variable, but as it only varies by 0.1 magnitude every four days this will be extremely difficult to detect. Your time may be better spent looking at ω. At a distance of 225 l.y., this double star has components of magnitudes 4.9 and 8.0 which will be resolved by a small telescope. Auriga's star clusters are even more rewarding. M36 (NGC 1960) contains around 60 stars, M37 (NGC 2099) about 150 and M38 (NGC 1912) about 100. They are all visible with binoculars but a telescope would give a finer view.

Canis Major
The Greater Dog

This constellation and Canis Minor, the Lesser Dog, are Orion's two hunting dogs. Like Orion this is a distinctive constellation containing some bright stars. Sirius (α, mag. -1.4), occasionally called the Dog Star, is the most noticeable and is the brightest star in the sky. Its name comes from the Greek for 'scorching'. It is a brilliant star and is less than 8.8 l.y. away from us. It has a much dimmer companion (mag. 8.5) which it overshadows and which can only be seen in the very largest of telescopes. Mirzam (β, mag. 2.0, 720 l.y.) and Adhara (ε, mag. 1.5, 490 l.y.) are both giant stars. Three star clusters in Canis Major are M41 (NGC 2287), NGC 2360 and NGC 2362. The most easily visible is M41, a cluster of about 50 stars, seen as a bright patch with the naked eye but more rewarding through binoculars. A telescope will be needed for both NGC 2360 and NGC 2362.

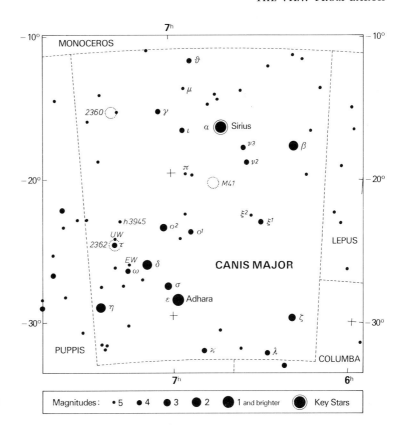

Magnitudes: • 5 • 4 ● 3 ● 2 ● 1 and brighter ◉ Key Stars

Capricornus
The Sea Goat

This constellation gave its name to the Tropic of Capricorn on Earth. In the distant past the Sun reached its most southerly point whilst in Capricornus. Although this point is now in Sagittarius, the tropic is still known by its original constellation name.

The most notable star for an observer is Giedi or Algedi (α Capricorni). This can be seen, with the naked eye or binoculars, to be two stars of magnitude 4.2 and 3.6 respectively. Dabih (β, mag. 3.1, 100 l.y.) and Deneb Algiedi (δ, mag. 2.9, 49 l.y.) also have companions. Yellow Dabih has a wide blue companion visible in binoculars. Deneb Algiedi, the brightest star in the constellation, is an eclipsing binary. Visible through small telescopes is globular cluster M30 (NGC 7099, 27,000 l.y.), which has a notably brighter nucleus.

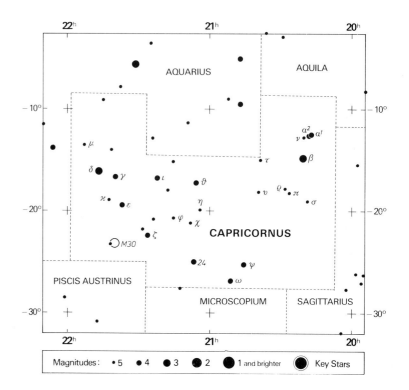

Cassiopeia

Cassiopeia was the Queen of Ethiopia, wife of King Cepheus and mother of Andromeda. She sits in the sky in a chair which forms the distinctive 'W' or 'M' shape of this constellation. As this is one of the northern circumpolar constellations, it will be an 'M' when above and a 'W' when below the pole. The five bright stars which mark the shape are Schedar (α, mag. 2.2, 120 l.y.), Caph (β, mag. 2.3, 42 l.y.), Cih (γ, mag. 2.5, 780 l.y.), Ruchbah (δ, mag. 2.7, 62 l.y.) and Segin (ε, mag. 3.4, 520 l.y.).

One of the most easily viewed double stars in this constellation is η (19 l.y.), which appears as a yellow (mag. 3.4) and a red (mag. 7.5) star when seen through a telescope. Binoculars will reveal the star cluster known as M52 (NGC 7654, 5000 l.y.). This will appear as a misty patch but will change into a group of individual stars if you observe it through a telescope. Also try your binoculars on NGC 663, a cluster of about 80 stars (7000 l.y.).

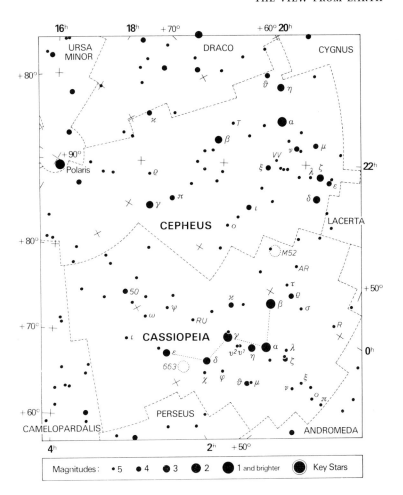

Centaurus
The Centaur

The two bright stars Rigil Kentaurus (α, mag. −0.3, 4.2 l.y.) and Hadar (β, mag. 0.6, 460 l.y.), and the fact that Centaurus is close to Crux makes it easy to find. Rigil Kentaurus is the third brightest star in the sky but a telescope will reveal it to be a pair of stars of magnitudes 0 and 1.4. Nearby is a star associated with this pair, Proxima Centauri, the closest star to the Sun. The brightest globular cluster in the sky is in Centaurus. It is ω Cen (NGC 5139, mag. 3.7, 17,000 l.y.); appearing as a hazy star to the naked eye, binoculars will resolve its outer limits into stars. Two other clusters to turn your binoculars on are NGC 5460 (1600 l.y.) and NGC 3766 (5500 l.y.), containing around 25 and 60 stars respectively.

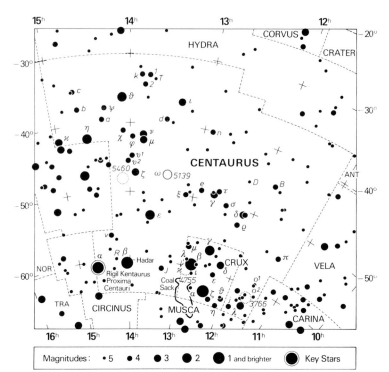

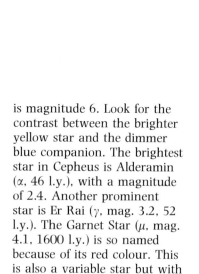

Cepheus (see map p. 69)

This constellation is named after Cepheus, the King of Ethiopia, who is in the sky near his Queen, Cassiopeia. It contains δ Cephei, the first of the Cepheid-type variables to be discovered (see p. 41). This star varies in brightness between magnitudes 3.5 and 4.4 over a period of 5.4 days. Binoculars will reveal that δ is a double star; its companion is magnitude 6. Look for the contrast between the brighter yellow star and the dimmer blue companion. The brightest star in Cepheus is Alderamin (α, 46 l.y.), with a magnitude of 2.4. Another prominent star is Er Rai (γ, mag. 3.2, 52 l.y.). The Garnet Star (μ, mag. 4.1, 1600 l.y.) is so named because of its red colour. This is also a variable star but with no regular period. Alfirk (β, mag. 3.2, 750 l.y.) has a companion of magnitude 8 which can be easily seen with a small telescope.

Crux (see map p. 70)
The Southern Cross

This constellation is a delight for southern observers. Although it is the smallest constellation in the sky, it is easily identified. Its brilliant stars stand out against the background of the Milky Way, which also silhouettes the dark nebula known as the Coal Sack (400 l.y.).

A telescope will reveal Acrux (α, mag. 0.9, 360 l.y.) to be a double star. The most spectacular object in this constellation is κ Crucis (also known as NGC 4755), the Jewel Box, which is one of the most famous and finest of star clusters. The 'jewels' are its brilliant coloured stars.

Cygnus
The Swan

This is one of the most easily recognized northern constellations. The five dominant stars form a cross, or more traditionally the basis for the depiction of a flying swan. The swan's head is Albireo (β, 390 l.y.), which is easily seen as two stars through binoculars, one yellow (mag. 3.1) and one blue-green (mag. 5.1). The tail is marked by the brightest star in the constellation, blue-white Deneb (α, mag. 1.3, 1800 l.y.), and the wings by blue-white δ (mag. 2.9, 160

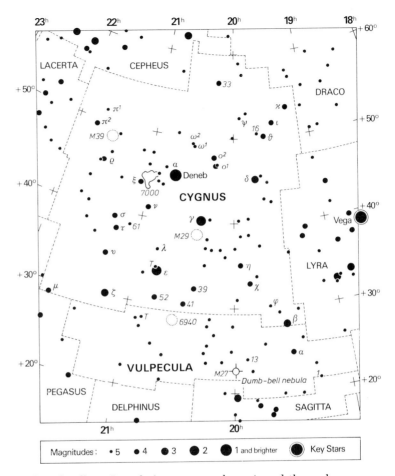

l.y.) and yellow Gienah (ε, mag. 2.5, 82 l.y.). Deneb is also one of the stars which form the Summer Triangle (see p. 65), the other two being Altair (α Aquilae) and Vega (α Lyrae). Sadr (γ, mag. 2.2, 750 l.y.) marks the bird's breast.

Do not leave Cygnus before looking at o, which is an unusually beautiful double

when viewed through binoculars. The stars are orange (mag. 3.8, 520 l.y.) and turquoise (mag. 4.0, 900 l.y.). Then turn your binoculars on the star cluster M39 (NGC 7092, 900 l.y.) and if it is a very clear night try to find the very faint NGC 7000 (1500 l.y.). This cloud of glowing gas up to 2° across is known as the North America

71

Nebula because its shape is so similar to the North American continent. One of the closest stars to Earth, 61 Cygni (11.1 l.y.) appears as a pair of orange dwarf stars (mags. 5.2 and 6.0) if observed through a small telescope.

Draco
The Dragon

This is one of the largest and one of the least well-defined constellations. Start by identifying the head and then follow the body as it winds itself around the north celestial pole. Eltanin, 'the dragon's head' (γ, mag. 2.2, 100 l.y.), is the brightest star in the constellation. Also in the head is the yellow supergiant Rastaban (β, mag. 2.8, 270 l.y.). The star Arrakis (μ, 85 l.y.) is a double, each of the partners being mag. 5.7. You'll need a telescope to separate them, but other doubles in Draco, v (both mag. 4.9, 62 l.y.) and ψ (mags. 4.6 and 5.8, 75 l.y.), are discernible through binoculars. NGC 6543 (mag. 9, 3600 l.y.) is a planetary nebula, but will only appear like a star through a suitably powerful telescope.

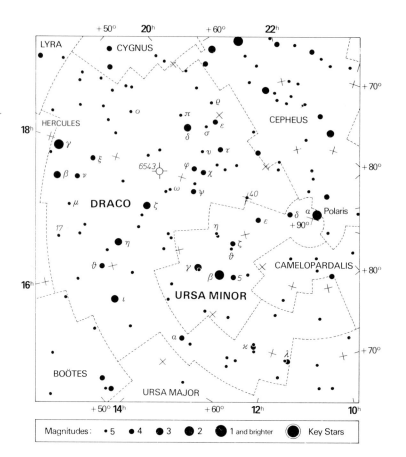

Gemini

The Twins

This is one of the zodiac constellations. It is marked by the twins, Castor and Pollux. Although Pollux is termed β, it is the brighter of the twins and the brightest star in this constellation. It is an orange giant of mag. 1.1 (36 l.y.). Castor (α, 46 l.y.) is not so straightforward. Seen with the naked eye it appears to be a single star of magnitude 1.6, but a telescope will reveal it to be two stars of magnitude 1.9 and 2.9 slowly orbiting each other. Although impossible to resolve, both of these stars are spectroscopic binaries. A telescope will also reveal that Wasat is a double star (δ, mags. 3.5 and 8.2, 59 l.y.). Alhena (γ, 85 l.y.) is a prominent single star of magnitude 1.9. The star cluster M35 (NGC 2168, 2800 l.y.) is easy to see, appearing as a hazy patch of light to the naked eye. The view is much improved through binoculars, and telescopes will resolve some of the 200 or so stars in the cluster. NGC 2392 is a planetary nebula of magnitude 10 which may look just like a star unless it is viewed through a sufficiently powerful telescope.

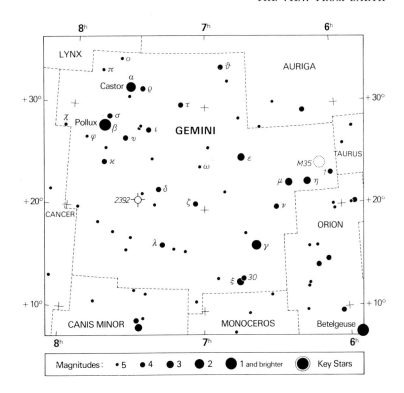

Magnitudes: •5 ● 4 ● 3 ● 2 ● 1 and brighter ⦿ Key Stars

Hercules

This is one of the largest constellations and contains no particularly bright stars. As a result Hercules as a whole is not easily recognizable. It does, however, contain objects of individual interest. Ras Algethi (α, 220 l.y.) is a red supergiant which fluctuates in brightness around magnitude 3.5. Telescopes will reveal it to be a double star; its companion is blue-green mag. 5.4. The yellow giant β (mag. 2.8, 100 l.y.) is brighter. The most recognizable part of the constellation is the 'keystone' area, marked by the four stars of Hercules' pelvis, near which is the globular cluster M13 (NGC 6205, 23,500 l.y.). This is the brightest globular cluster in the northern hemisphere; although it is over 100 l.y. in diameter, it looks like a fuzzy star to the naked eye. A globular cluster at greater distance is M92 (NGC 6341, 25,500 l.y.). You'll be able to make this out in binoculars but it will be more obvious with a telescope.

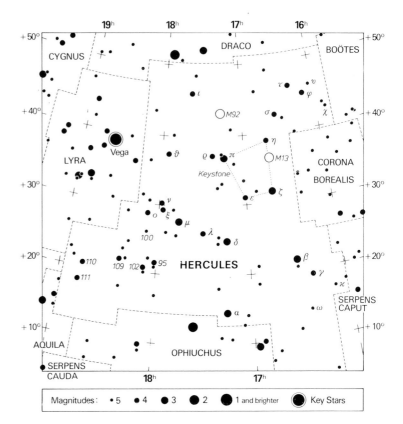

Leo
The Lion

It is easy to imagine how the stars in this constellation became known as the lion. The curve of the head and the limits of the body are easily found. Regulus (α, mag. 1.4, 85 l.y.) is the brightest star, followed by Denebola, which marks the lion's tail (β, mag. 2.1, 39 l.y.). Algieba (γ, 100 l.y.) is revealed as a pair of 'golden' stars of magnitudes 2.3 and 3.5 when seen through a telescope. The two pairs of galaxies are also well worth looking at, but you'll need a telescope, a dark sky and some patience as they have low magnitude values. Try M65 (NGC 3623, mag. 9) and M66 (3627, mag. 9) at 20 million l.y., followed by M95 (NGC 3351, mag. 10) and M96 (NGC 3368, mag. 9) at 22 million l.y.

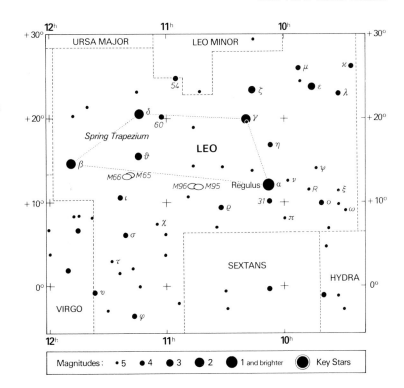

Lyra
The Lyre

This is a small but prominent constellation due to the fact that it contains the star Vega, the fifth brightest in the sky. Vega (α, mag. 0.0) is a brilliant blue-white star 26 l.y. away. Much further away from us is Sheliak (β 300 l.y.), which small telescopes will reveal is a double star. The individual stars orbit each other just over once every thirteen days, Sheliak varies in magnitude from 3.4 to 4.3 as the stars pass in front of each other.

Lyra also contains an example of a rare double double star. With very good eyesight, but more easily with binoculars, ε (120 l.y.) will prove to be two stars of magnitudes 4.7 and 5.1. Only a telescope will show that each of these stars is itself a double star. Then turn your telescope to M57 (NGC 6720, 2000 l.y.), which is more commonly known as the Ring Nebula—the famous planetary nebula which looks like a smoke ring. In a small telescope it will appear as a misty disc; larger telescopes will reveal the central hole.

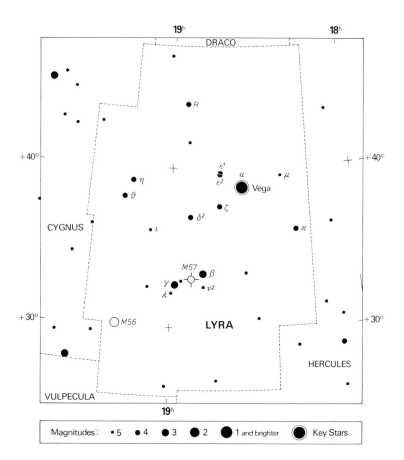

Orion
The Hunter

This is one of the most distinctive of all the constellations and the stars outlining the figure of Orion are easily found. His shoulders and knees are marked by four bright ones, his belt by three more, and his sword, hanging from his belt, by the Orion Nebula. Betelgeuse (α, 310 l.y.) is a noticeably red star; a large unstable giant which changes in brightness between around magnitudes 0.4 and 1.3. Although it is termed α, the brightest star in the constellation is Rigel (β, 910 l.y.), a blue-white giant with a magnitude of 0.1. Bellatrix (γ, mag. 1.6, 360 l.y.) and Saiph (κ, mag. 2.1, 70 l.y.) complete the four stars which mark the boundary of Orion's figure. Mintaka (δ, 2300 l.y.), Alnilam (ε, mag. 1.7, 1200 l.y.) and Alnitak (ζ, mag. 1.8, 1100 l.y.) are the stars which mark his belt. Mintaka will appear to the naked eye as a magnitude 2.2 star; binoculars will reveal a magnitude 6.9 companion. Very close observation of the main star will also reveal that this is an eclipsing binary whose magnitude varies by 0.1 about every 6 days.

The Orion Nebula (M42, NGC 1976) is in the hunter's sword. It is an enormous cloud of gas and dust, 15 l.y.

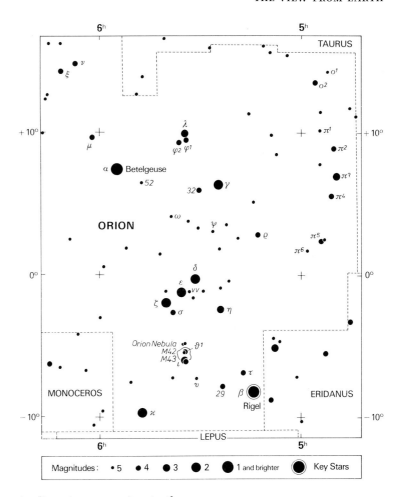

in diameter, appearing to the naked eye as a cloudy patch. Powerful telescopes will reveal θ′ towards the centre of the nebula to be four stars of magnitudes 5.1, 6.7, 6.7 and 7.9. These are commonly known as the Trapezium. The nebula M43 (NGC 1982) close by is centred on a single star of magnitude 9.

Pisces
The Fishes

Pisces is a faint constellation which is known primarily for being on the path of the ecliptic, and in particular because the Sun is within Pisces when it crosses the celestial equator from the southern to the northern celestial hemisphere. Al Rischa (α, 98 l.y.) is the star which marks the knot tying the two fishes together. A telescope will reveal that it is a double star (mags. 4.2 and 5.1). The brightest star in the constellation is the yellow giant η Pisces (mag. 3.6, 140 l.y.). A good telescope will also reveal the dim spiral galaxy M74 (NGC 628) which is 22.5 million l.y. away (mag. 9).

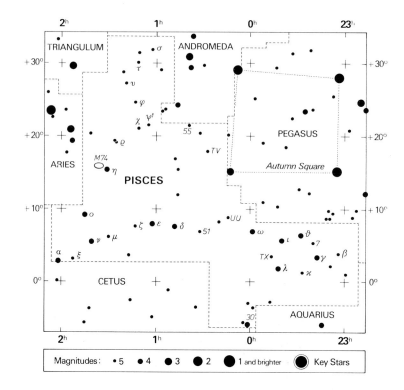

78

Sagittarius
The Archer

Sagittarius has much to offer the observer. It is one of the ancient constellations lying on the ecliptic and marking the most southerly point of the Sun's path. The centre of our Galaxy lies in the direction of Sagittarius and this is a very rich and distinctive area of the Milky Way. Sagittarius is a centaur, half man, half beast, aiming his arrow at Scorpius. His bow is marked by three individual stars, the orange giants Kaus Borealis (λ, mag. 2.8, 98 l.y.), Kaus Meridonalis (δ, mag. 2.7, 82 l.y.) and the brightest star in the constellation, Kaus Australis (ε, mag. 1.9, 85 l.y.). This is another of the constellations where the brightest star is not termed α.

The real splendours of Sagittarius are a host of star clusters and nebulae. Among them is the Lagoon Nebula (M8, NGC 6523), 5000 l.y. away and visible to the naked eye. You'll need binoculars to see the nearby Trifid Nebula (M20, NGC 6514), or better still a telescope. Just on the edge of the constellation is the Omega or Horseshoe Nebula (M17, NGC 6618), visible through binoculars. The globular cluster M22 (NGC 6656), 10,000 l.y. away, is one of the finest of its type; it is just visible with the naked

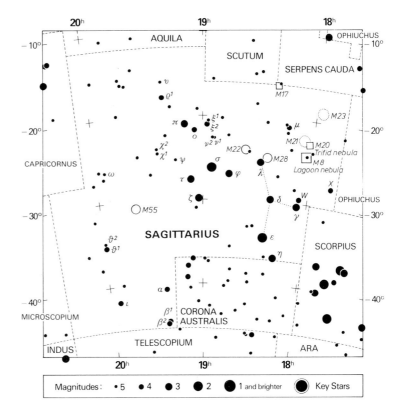

eye and easily detected with binoculars. Binoculars will also reveal the globular cluster M55 (NGC 6809) and the widespread cluster M23 (NGC 6494).

79

Scorpius
The Scorpion

A beautiful constellation whose stars actually do draw out the form of a scorpion. Bright Antares (α, mag. 1.0, 330 l.y.) marks the 'head' of the creature. It is a red supergiant whose name means 'the rival of Mars'. Other stars outline the body and provide the sting of the scorpion's tail; the most notable are Dschubba (δ, mag. 2.3, 550 l.y.), ε (mag. 2.3, 65 l.y.), θ (mag. 1.9, 910 l.y.) and Shaula, the sting (λ, mag. 1.6, 270 l.y.). There are a number of double stars: Graffias (β, mags. 2.6 and 4.9, 800 l.y.), ν (mags. 4.0 and 6.3, 550 l.y.), ξ (mags. 4.8 and 5.1, 85 l.y.) and σ (mags. 2.9 and 8.5, 590 l.y.), but a telescope will be needed to separate them. Higher magnification telescopes will reveal that ν is a double double and ξ is a multiple star.

The naked eye will be able to see the star clusters M7, containing around eighty stars (NGC 6475, 800 l.y.), and NGC 6231 with around 120 stars. Binoculars reveal star cluster M6 (NGC 6405, mag. 4.2, 2000 l.y.) and globular clusters M4 (NGC 6121, mag. 6, 7000 l.y.) and M80 (NGC 6093, mag. 7.2, 27,000 l.y.).

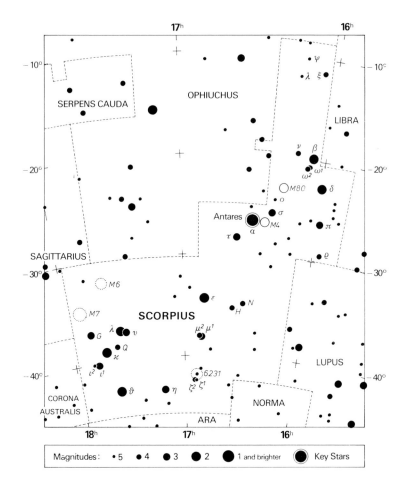

Taurus
The Bull

This is one of the better known constellations, to astronomers and non-astronomers alike, as its bright stars and shape make it easy to see in the sky. Although it is described as the bull, only the head and shoulders are easily drawn around the stars. Its face is formed by the distinctive V-shaped cluster of stars, the Hyades, with its horns stretching out to the stars El Nath (β, mag. 1.7, 130 l.y.) and ζ (mag. 3.0, 490 l.y.). The bull's eye is marked by the red giant star Aldebaran (α, mag. 0.9, 68 l.y.), which appears to be part of the Hyades but is totally unrelated and is in fact much closer to us than the cluster.

The Hyades star cluster (150 l.y.) is best viewed through binoculars when you will be able to see more of the 200 or so stars in the cluster. A second cluster in Taurus, of about 100 stars, is the Pleiades (410 l.y.) or Seven Sisters (also known as M45), which is the brightest star cluster in the sky. The Pleiades cover about 1° of sky compared to the 5° of the Hyades. At least six stars can be seen with the naked eye, or seven if you have good eyesight. Binoculars will multiply that number

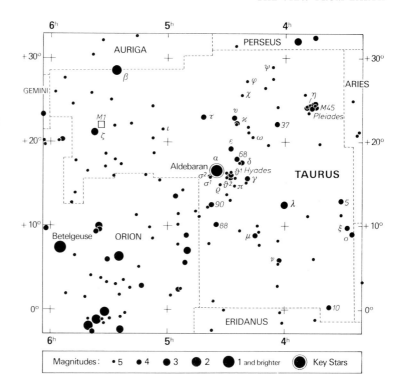

Magnitudes: •5 ●4 ●3 ●2 ●1 and brighter ◉ Key Stars

considerably.

Close to ζ Tauri is the Crab Nebula (5000 l.y.), also known as M1 or NGC 1952. This is the remains of a supernova which exploded in 1054. Also worth looking at are λ (330 l.y.), an eclipsing binary varying between mag. 3.3 and 3.8 every four days and ϕ (mag. 5.0 and 8.4; 290 l.y.), a double star which will be best observed through binoculars or a small telescope.

81

Ursa Major
The Great Bear

This is one of the largest and also the best known of all the constellations. The seven bright stars that make up the tail and back of the bear and which are known as the Plough, or the Big Dipper, make the constellation easy to find. Two of these stars point to Polaris, the Pole Star, in the constellation of Ursa Minor, the Lesser Bear. They are Dubhe (α, mag. 1.8, 75 l.y.) and Merak (β, mag. 2.4, 62 l.y.). The others are Phekda (γ, mag. 2.4, 75 l.y.), Megrez (δ, mag. 3.3, 65 l.y.), Alioth (ε, varying mag. 1.7 to 1.8, 62 l.y.), Mizar (ζ, mag. 2.3, 60 l.y.) and Benetnash (η, mag. 1.9, 110 l.y.). Keen eyesight will reveal Mizar's companion star Alcor (mag. 4.0). Mizar also has other companions—see p. 37.

There are also several objects of interest away from the area of the Plough. Point your telescope at ν (150 l.y.) and it will be revealed as a double star: a 3.5 mag. golden giant with a 9.9 mag. companion. Also try the two galaxies M81 (NGC 3031, mag. 7, 18 million l.y.) and M82 (NGC 3034, mag. 8, 18 million l.y.), which are very close to each other. M81 is a spiral galaxy which appears as a hazy, oval patch of light with a brighter centre; the

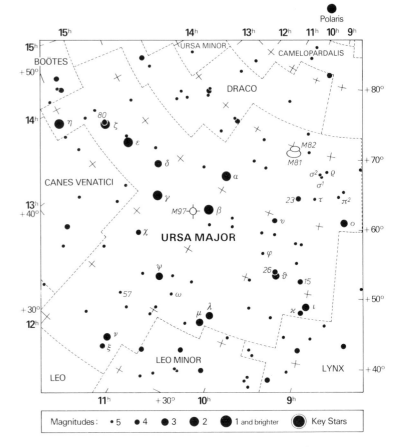

fainter M82 appears as a blurred streak of light.

Ursa Minor (see map p. 72)
The Lesser Bear

Together with nearby Ursa Major, this is one of the first constellations that observers in the northern hemisphere learn. This is because it contains Polaris, the star that is within 1° of the north celestial pole and consequently not only always appears at a northerly altitude equal to the observer's latitude but also appears to remain still while the other stars move around it. Polaris is α Ursae Minoris (700 l.y.). It is a Cepheid variable which changes in brightness every four days between mags. 1.9 and 2.1. It also has a fainter (mag. 9) companion which telescopes will reveal. The other notable stars in this constellation are Kochab (β, mag. 2.1, 95 l.y.) and Pherkad (γ, mag. 3.1, 230 l.y.), jointly called the pole's guardians.

Virgo
The Virgin

This is the second largest constellation in the sky and is interesting primarily for the galaxies it contains. The brightest star Spica (α, mag. 1.0, 260 l.y.) shines alone. Porrima (γ, mag. 2.8, 36 l.y.) is in fact a double star, each of the two stars being mag. 3.5. They have an orbit period of 172 years and as they are presently moving closer and closer together it becomes more and more difficult for an observer with a small telescope to see the two components. Although there are a number of galaxies in this constellation they are all equally difficult to see. Try the elliptical giant galaxy M49 (NGC 4472, mag. 8.4) first; it is marginally the easiest to see. Binoculars combined with keen eyesight will pick it up as a hazy patch. Telescopes with low power will be needed for the others. You'll find four elliptical galaxies in two fields of view: M59 (NGC 4621, mag. 10) and M60 (NGC 4649, mag. 9) in one, and M84 (NGC 4374, mag. 9)

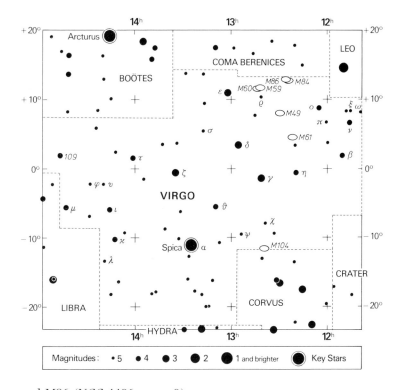

and M86 (NGC 4406, mag. 9) in the other. The spiral galaxy M104 (NGC 4594) is magnitude 8.5. It is seen edge on and is often called the Sombrero because of its similarity to the hat.

83

8 · Our Local Star, the Sun

The only star we can examine at close quarters is our own star, the Sun. Other stars appear either as individual pin-points of light or as hazy patches denoting a group of stars. The Sun is the only star that gives both amateur and professional astronomers a chance to look at such a body in detail. In many ways, too, it is an ideal object to observe. It dominates our sky day in, day out and it is easily noticeable without any special instrumentation. There are, however, serious hazards involved in sungazing. *It is dangerous to look at the Sun*, with or without binoculars or a telescope. Do not even attempt the briefest of glimpses through an unprotected instrument, as light from the Sun can damage the sensitive retina at the back of the eye. This damage is irreparable and can result in blindness. We now know the problems connected with observing the Sun and do not need to suffer as others have done in the past. It is thought that Galileo's habit of observing the Sun through the newly-invented telescope contributed to his blindness in old age.

There are two ways of observing the Sun safely. One is by viewing it directly through a telescope with a proper protection filter. The other is by projecting the Sun's image. The first method is only mentioned here because many people know that the Sun can be observed through filters. It is not, however, to be recommended unless you have the correct equipment and know what you are doing. The 'sun filters' supplied with some telescopes are not safe. They can crack with the solar heat and it is almost impossible to move away quickly enough to avoid eye damage. If you must look at the Sun directly through a telescope you must use a Herschel wedge which reflects only a very small proportion of the light entering the telescope to the eyepiece. And even the Herschel wedge must be used in conjunction with a dark filter on the eyepiece. There are safe solar filters available which protect the eye against both visible and invisible radiation, and the telescope against the effects of heat. The most common type is made of metallized Mylar plastic which usually turns the Sun blue. Metal-on-glass filters through which the Sun appears in a more natural tint are more durable but more costly.

The best way of observing the Sun is by projecting the image. This method is perfectly safe and quite simple. Normally the light from a star will pass through your telescope or binoculars to form an image on your retina. With

A partial eclipse of the Sun projected through binoculars.

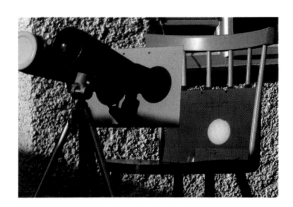

the projection method the image is formed on a piece of white card or paper which is placed at the eye end of the telescope, or at one eye end of a pair of binoculars. The focus of your instrument can be adjusted to produce a sharp image on the card. You will need to place a further piece of card around the body of the instrument to stop the projected image being obscured by direct sunlight. You could also construct a projection box to attach to your telescope which would give you an even more contrasted image.

If you use the projection method you can record sunspots in pencil on the paper screen. These dark patches on the Sun's visible surface mark relatively cool areas. They are made up of a darker central umbra, surrounded by a lighter area known as the penumbra. The darker an area appears, the cooler the temperature. Galileo's work on sunspots brought them to public attention but it was the German Jesuit Christopher Scheiner who made the first comprehensive study of them in 1611–25. From his observations he deduced how long the Sun took to rotate and he also detected the bright patches known as faculae. These are normally seen near the edge of the Sun's disc; they are generally associated with sunspot groups, although they can appear alone.

The number of sunspots varies from year to year over a cycle of 11.1 years. A cycle starts at sunspot minimum when there may be no spots. The spots then begin to appear at a latitude approximately 30° north or south of the solar equator. As time goes on they emerge nearer and nearer the equator. The maximum number of spots occurs four to five years after the start of the cycle; they then gradually become fewer until the start of the next cycle. It is possible to see the spots of two cycles on the Sun's surface at the same time. The old spots will occur by the equator and the new ones at higher latitudes either side of it.

The first person systematically to record the paths and cycles of the spots was E. Walter Maunder, who worked at the Royal Observatory at Greenwich at the start of this century. When the numbers and positions of the spots are plotted on a graph they look like butterfly wings and these records are called butterfly diagrams. Try observing and recording sunspots on a regular basis for yourself. If you do this for long enough, a cycle will start to emerge. The last minimum was in late 1986 so you could start observing for the next maximum in 1990. Try daily observations when there is a chance of continuous sunshine. You should be able to determine the rotation of the Sun by noting the apparent movement of the spots across the Sun's surface. A spot takes about two weeks to appear from behind the eastern limb, travel across the disc and depart around the western limb. Detailed observations have shown that the Sun rotates in 26.8 days at the equator, rising to 28.2 days at 30° and 30.8 days at 60°. Remember to use the same equipment (for example, the same magnification) at all times so that the diameter of the Sun's disc is constant and you can easily compare your observations.

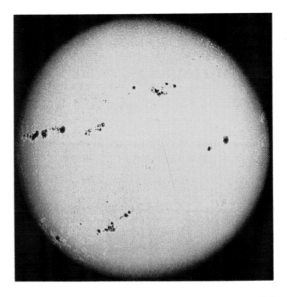

Sunspots; cooler areas on the Sun's visible surface.

It is well worth making the effort to observe a solar eclipse. There are usually two and occasionally three per year over the world as a whole, but the chances are you'll have to travel some way to see one. The last total eclipse visible from anywhere in England was on 29 June 1927. The next is on 11 August 1999. A solar eclipse occurs when the Sun's disc is partially or wholly obscured by the Moon's disc. As the Moon passes between the Sun and the Earth it stops some of the Sun's light from reaching Earth and forms a shadow on the Earth's surface. An observer standing within this shadow can observe the eclipse. Although the Sun's diameter is nearly 400 times larger than the Moon's, they appear to be almost the same size when viewed from Earth because the Sun is nearly 400 times further away than the Moon. Only those standing in the central part of the Moon's shadow, known as the umbra, will see a total eclipse; those in the outer penumbra will see the Sun only partly obscured. An annular eclipse occurs when the relative distances of Sun and Moon mean that the Moon's disc is too small to cover the Sun's disc

Solar prominences photographed during the solar eclipse in July 1973.

completely. In this case a ring of light is visible around the black disc of the Moon when the Sun and Moon are aligned.

The maximum length of time a total eclipse can take is 7 minutes 31 seconds. It is amazing how quickly the time will go and so you must be prepared if you have an opportunity to see one. Decide in advance if there is any particular observation you want to make, or whether you are simply going to sit back and enjoy the experience. It is unlikely you'll have time to do both. The usual precautions for observing the Sun must still be followed during the partial phases of an eclipse. They can only be dispensed with during totality and must be used again as soon as the second partial phase approaches. Consequently you'll need to have an accurate timekeeper with you. Set an alarm watch to sound a little before totality ends so you are warned of the coming sunlight.

Look out for the Sun's corona. This is the outer

atmosphere which is only visible to the unaided eye during a total eclipse, appearing as a halo around the obscured disc. At totality you may also see what are known as prominences—regions of hot hydrogen gas flaring out from the edge of the Sun's disc. One further spectacular sight to look out for is the diamond-ring effect. This can occur at the moment a total eclipse is about to start or about to end. A bright flash of sunlight appears just as the Sun is on the point of disappearing or emerging from behind the Moon. It is caused by the edge of the Sun peeping through the uneven edge of the Moon. The overall effect is like a diamond ring.

Although the eclipse itself is absorbing enough, there can be other interesting and non-astronomical effects to watch out for. The effect of the changing amount of sunlight on the area around you can be fascinating. The air temperature will change causing the 'eclipse wind'. You may also be lucky enough to see a planet or a bright star in the darkened sky. During the total eclipse of 29 May 1919 a group of astronomers from the Royal Observatory, Greenwich, photographed the positions of stars lying close to the Sun. These were found to be displaced from their known positions according to the predictions of the general theory of relativity, which states that light rays should be deflected as they pass close to a massive body such as the Sun. The work of the Greenwich group of astronomers had confirmed an important part of Einstein's general theory of relativity.

Finally, don't forget the other everyday occasions when the Sun can provide a spectacular sight. The atmosphere on the horizon can affect how our star appears. The light is refracted to make the Sun appear oblate, as a squashed disc, while scattering caused by the atmosphere can make it appear deep orange or red.

RIGHT *The diamond ring effect is seen in this photograph of a solar eclipse taken on 16 February 1980 in Ngomeni, Kenya.*

This view of the Sun setting over the city of London is a regular sight from the Old Royal Observatory at Greenwich.

Solar eclipses
(up to the end of this century)

Date		Type	Duration	Path across Earth
1988	18 Mar	Total	3 min. 46 sec.	Indian Ocean, E. Indies, Pacific
	11 Sept	Annular	7 min.	Indian Ocean, S. of Australia, Antarctic
1989	7 Mar	Partial		Arctic
	31 Aug	Partial		Antarctic
1990	26 Jan	Annular		Antarctic
	22 July	Total	2 min. 33 sec.	Finland, USSR, Pacific
1991	15–16 Jan	Annular	9 min.	Australia, New Zealand, Pacific
	11 July	Total	6 min. 54 sec.	Pacific, Central America, Brazil
1992	4–5 Jan	Annular	12 min.	Central Pacific
	30 Jun	Total	5 min. 20 sec.	S. Atlantic
	24 Dec	Partial		Arctic
1993	21 May	Partial		Arctic
	13 Nov	Partial		Antarctic
1994	10 May	Annular	7 min.	Pacific, Mexico, USA, Canada, Atlantic
	3 Nov	Total	4 min. 23 sec.	Peru, Brazil, S. Atlantic
1995	29 Apr	Annular	7 min.	S. Pacific, Peru, Brazil, S. Atlantic
	24 Oct	Total	2 min. 5 sec.	Iran, India, E. Indies, Pacific
1996	17 Apr	Partial		Antarctica
	12 Oct	Partial		Arctic
1997	9 Mar	Total	2 min. 50 sec.	USSR, Arctic
	2 Sept	Partial		Antarctic
1998	26 Feb	Total	3 min. 56 sec.	Pacific, S. of Panama, Atlantic
	22 Aug	Annular	3 min.	Indian Ocean, E. Indies, Pacific
1999	16 Feb	Annular	1 min.	Indian Ocean, Australia, Pacific
	11 Aug	Total	2 min. 23 sec.	Atlantic, England, France, Central Europe, Turkey, India

9 · Last, but not Least

Most people assume that you need to have a telescope to be an astronomer. This just isn't true. The telescope was only invented at the beginning of the seventeenth century and, although its use in the past three hundred or so years has revolutionized our knowledge of the universe, we had already learnt an enormous amount by just using our eyes. There were at least two thousand years of astronomy before the telescope. The mathematician Eratosthenes used his naked eye to measure shadows cast by the Sun in his calculation of the Earth's size in around 200 BC. The Greek astronomer Hipparchus found the size and distance of the Moon by measuring the diameter of the Earth's shadow cast on the Moon during eclipses. The Polish astronomer Nicholas Copernicus used naked-eye observations of the planets' motions to develop his theory of a Sun-centred Solar System published in 1543. Naked-eye measurements were used by Johannes Kepler as the basis for his three laws of planetary motion, which became the basis of our present model of the Solar System.

The naked eye can be used for simple stargazing or more detailed observational work. It is also the easiest and friendliest way to get to know the stars. You can observe the heavens anywhere as long as the sky is clear. There is no need to carry around complicated instrumentation. You can also observe with family and friends without having to wait until it is your turn to look through the telescope. Once you do graduate to binoculars or a telescope you'll not only be appreciative of the new sights they offer, but you'll also find it much easier to use the instruments. As you move from eye to binoculars to telescope, your field of view, the area of the sky you are looking at, becomes smaller and smaller. At the same time the magnification of that area of sky could be getting larger and larger. With the naked eye you can see around 80° of sky before you need to move your head. Stationary binoculars show around 6° of sky and a telescope 1°. As the field of view decreases you start to see only part of once familiar star patterns. Increasingly large instruments will reveal fainter and fainter stars. It is very useful to be so familiar with the naked-eye stars that you can use them as markers to find your way around these new and detailed areas of sky. So don't get lost in the details of space before you can fully appreciate the overall picture.

All sorts of stellar objects are visible to the naked eye: single, double and variable stars; clusters, nebulae and galaxies. Whatever the object you are observing, it is worth taking a few precautions before you start. Your choice of observing site will affect what you see. It is best to get away from any sort of artificial light. City lights affect the sky to such an extent that they make it impossible to observe objects near the horizon, as well as increasing the background light over the remainder of the sky. The light from a star is so absorbed by the atmosphere that a star of magnitude 4 at the zenith, directly above the astronomer's head, will only appear as a dimmer magnitude 6 star just above the horizon. When astronomers first started observing from Greenwich in 1675 it was a village in the countryside. By the middle of the twentieth

century it had become engulfed by London and the increasing use of city lights meant that some of the observatory's work had to be pursued using the darker skies of Sussex. It is possible to observe from a city, but it is very limiting. The naked eye can determine stars down to a minimum brightness of magnitude 6.1 in a dark sky, but only to around magnitude 4.3 in city conditions.

On the other hand, you can use these less than ideal conditions to your advantage. A light-polluted sky will only be dark enough to show up the brightest stars, which are usually those that give a constellation its distinctive pattern. This can make the constellation shapes easier to find as the background is not confused by other stars. Once you are familiar with these patterns you can graduate to darker skies which show many more stars. For every magnitude you drop, you can see about 3.5 times more stars. The stars you have learnt from observing in the city can be used as a basis for finding your way amongst the larger numbers of stars visible in darker skies. Even within the city some locations are better than others. If you can, find a park or common which

The lights of London as viewed from the Old Royal Observatory at Greenwich on any evening throughout the year. This light pollution severely restricts observing.

doesn't have street lights. Should you prefer to stay in your own garden, turn off your room lights to make your locality as dark as possible.

Wherever you are do not expect too much too quickly. When you first go from the light of the house into the dark garden you are not adjusted to the dark. In the same way as when lights suddenly go off in a room or when you walk into a darkened cinema, you can see very little. In the cinema the usherette has a torch to guide you to your seat. It is only after you have been sitting down for a few minutes that you can make out the people to the side of you or the bag you fell over when you first came in. When you go out into the garden and look up you will see some bright stars but as time goes on this number will increase. So, don't give up after the first ten minutes. Stay for at least another ten minutes to give your eyes a chance to get adjusted. Full dark adaptation takes about twenty-five minutes.

You need cloudless night skies to go observing, but this usually means that the temperature of the surrounding air will be low, unless you live in the tropics. Standing outside for half an hour is likely to make even the hardiest of observers feel cold if they are unprepared. Wear suitable clothing. You can lose a lot of body heat through your head so a hat is essential. Gloves, extra jumpers and thick socks may also be needed.

Some astronomers have worn heated suits for when they are observing for long and cold stretches. A hot drink in a vacuum flask and a hot water bottle are enough to satisfy others. Make sure you have all these things as well as a plan of what to observe. You cannot keep running in and out of the house for something you have forgotten as the change in light will affect your eyes. As time goes on you'll know what you need and your preparation will be automatic.

Some of the planets are easily visible with the naked eye and can at first glance be mistaken for stars. The word planet is derived from the original Greek term which described these bodies and literally means 'wanderer', or more loosely 'wandering star'. The planets can be distinguished from the stars because they will appear to move against the star background. They are also disc-shaped compared to the pin-points of light which are the stars. A pair of binoculars will soon confirm whether you are looking at a planet or a star. The instrument will enlarge the planet's disc shape and make it more obvious, but the stars will always appear as pin-points of light whether seen through binoculars or with the naked eye. Planets are also often the first visible objects as night falls or the last to be seen as daylight starts.

As we saw on p. 14, the planets are always found within a limited area of sky which is known as the zodiac. This circular band of sky is centred on the ecliptic and extends to about 9° either side of it. The planets, the Sun and Moon all move within this area. Those planets most easily confused with stars are Venus, Mars, Jupiter and Saturn. At its faintest Venus has a magnitude of −3.9. It is sometimes referred to as the Morning Star or the Evening Star because of its brilliant appearance at dawn and dusk. The other planets, Mercury, Uranus, Neptune and Pluto, are more difficult to observe and it is very unlikely that you will mistake them for bright stars.

'Shooting stars' similarly have no place in this book. A shooting star is not a star, but a meteor. These small, fast-moving particles burn up as they enter the Earth's atmosphere, appearing as short-lived streaks of light in the sky. This is why they are known as shooting stars. They occur randomly and also in showers, which result when the Earth crosses a stream of particles. All meteor particles are produced by cometary decay. As meteors and comets are more closely associated with planets than they are with stars, you'll find them described more fully in the companion guide to this book, *The Greenwich Guide to the Planets*.

The naked-eye observer gradually becomes familiar and at ease with the night sky. This base can then be used to realize the true potential of an instrument, whether binoculars or telescope. *Binoculars* are often overlooked as an astronomical instrument but they have many advantages. They are relatively inexpensive to buy, easy to use and adaptable for other pursuits such as bird-watching. Most people are not aware of the detail that can be seen by using binoculars. Double and variable stars, star clusters, nebulae and galaxies are all revealed, as well as other subjects not covered in this book, such as mountains and craters on the Moon, and planets and their moons. When you first look at the sky through binoculars you'll be amazed by the increase in the number of stars you can see. There are at least 43,000 stars in the sky with magnitudes of up to 8; binoculars will show all of them. Use the constellation patterns that you have already learnt to find your way about.

If you already have a pair of binoculars that may have been bought for other than astronomi-

91

The planet Venus is close to the horizon. The Pleiades and the Hyades are above it and to the left respectively.

cal reasons, try them out—they are bound to offer new views. Any binoculars can be used for astronomy, but some are better than others. All binoculars are referred to by using two numbers, such as 7 × 50, or 8 × 40. The first number refers to the magnifying power of the instrument, the second to the diameter in millimetres of the front, objective lenses. The novice stargazer may wrongly assume that the greater the magnifying power the better the instrument, and hence the better the view. A high magnifying power can be useful when looking at specific objects, such as double stars or star clusters, but it has disadvantages. The higher the magnification, the smaller the field of view, i.e. the area of sky being observed. A lower magnification and a larger field of view will make it easier to find your way about the sky. Higher magnification can also mean magnification of the imperfections within the binoculars, and any slight movement of the hands holding them will be so exaggerated as to make the stars wobble and dance in the field of view. Stay with a maximum magnification of 8 if your binoculars are to be hand-held.

The size of the lenses is important because it indicates the light-gathering power of the instrument; the bigger the aperture, the brighter the stars. If a star is to be seen clearly, the instrument needs to gather in as much light as possible rather than simply magnifying it and consequently spreading it out. When choosing a pair of binoculars consider the aperture and magnifying properties carefully. It is best to go for a pair which offer all round use, with an aperture which will gather plenty of light, but will not be so large that the binoculars are unwieldy or inconvenient to use, and a not too high magnifying power. Try any of these, or similar combinations; 7×35, 7×40, 8×40, 8×50.

Aperture is equally important when it comes to choosing a *telescope*. In this case the measurement refers to the diameter of the main lens or mirror. The traditional telescope that uses lenses is known as a refractor, but the reflector, which uses a mirror to collect the light, is becoming increasingly popular among astronomers. Another important characteristic of a telescope is its focal length, which is used to calculate the f ratio. The focal length of a telescope is the distance from the main lens or mirror to the focus, near where the eyepiece is placed to receive the image. The focal length divided by the aperture gives the telescope's f ratio. For example, a telescope with an aperture of 7.5 centimetres and a focal length of 75 centimetres is called an f/10. Telescopes perform differently according to the f ratio. Your choice of telescope will depend on what you are going to use it for. Close double stars, the Sun, the Moon and the planets require high power and sharp resolution, that is ratios of f/12 and upwards. Star clusters, nebulae and galaxies need low powers and wider fields of view, so short-focus instruments of f/6 and below are more suitable here. The middle ranges will best suit the all-round observer.

However, no-one should acquire a telescope until their interest is great enough to make it worth buying a quality instrument. The observer's aims, surroundings and pocket should all be taken into consideration and the telescope chosen to suit individual needs. Too many people buy a telescope expecting it to reveal the heavens and then abandon it in disillusion. A telescope will only work at its best in the hands of a practised observer. And there is no better way to practise than to stargaze without an instrument.

The three bright spots in the centre of this picture are, from top to bottom, Saturn, Mars and α Librae. The star β Librae is at the top left.

Index

References to illustrations appear in italics.

The Greek alphabet

Text	Map	Name
α	α	alpha
β	β	beta
γ	γ	gamma
δ	δ	delta
ε	ε	epsilon
ζ	ζ	zeta
η	η	eta
θ	ϑ	theta
ι	ι	iota
κ	$\varkappa$	kappa
λ	λ	lambda
μ	μ	mu
ν	ν	nu
ξ	ξ	xi
o	o	omicron
π	π	pi
ρ	ϱ	rho
σ	σ	sigma
τ	τ	tau
υ	υ	upsilon
ϕ	φ	phi
χ	χ	chi
ψ	ψ	psi
ω	ω	omega